MAKE
WORLDS

Kris Van den Driessche

The code of Hathor deciphered
The disastrous half-precession cycle

europe books

ISBN 979-12-201-0488-3
First edition: December 2020

The code of Hathor deciphered
The disastrous half-precession cycle

*"Maybe it's better to stay at a superficial level,
keeping the own prejudices…
because the deeper we dig, the more awkward
our existence becomes."*

CHAPTER 1
WHAT ARE GODS?

In order to understand our past, we can investigate it by means of geological formations, fossils and archaeological artefacts, as well as by making deductions about the nature and the behaviour of planets and stars. However, as we go further into the past, the less evidence remains and the fewer answers we obtain. But in this case, we still have a rich archive of old legends and traditions.

The very old legends and traditions have now become rather unclear: the older they are, the less comprehensible they become. As a result, we started to classify them as myths and, because of their strong significance, some of these traditions were the origin of religious beliefs.

These old texts, myths and beliefs need to be understood. Who are these gods and what were the events they talk about?

First of all, we are finding more or less identical old legends and traditions, dispersed remarkably widely across the whole world. I say "remarkably" because they deal with texts from before the first-known temples and other structures. We would not expect our ancestors to have had the same stories and traditions all over the world, but they did. Either there were once advanced civilisations living together on a global scale, or our ancestors were talking about major events that happened all over the world. Or of course, both assumptions could be true.

Let's take, for instance, the traditions relating to duality. From the Far East to India, Sumer and Egypt, all the way over to the Mayan civilisation in the West, everyone had the same knowledge of the duality between north and south, up and down, visible and invisible. The concept of duality comes from our sky, the "firmament". You have the Northern Hemisphere and the Southern Hemisphere. Living on the northern side of the earth, one can see the Northern Hemisphere, the visible hemisphere, while the Southern Hemisphere is invisible to those living in the north. The stars in the Northern Hemisphere are up in the sky, while the stars from the Southern Hemisphere are down in darkness. This means that the gods of these traditions were stars.

In the Middle Ages, the church didn't understand this concept as they thought that the world was flat. So their interpretation was that there are stars, gods and angels visible up in Heaven, while other stars, angels or devils were invisible, down in the earth, and they called this Hell. This misinterpretation then gave rise to an erroneous concept of good having its home in Heaven and evil having its roots deep in the earth, in Hell. From the Middle Ages, through the Renaissance and until the beginning of the Industrial Age, the Church abused this misconception to propagate fear in order to gain more power, telling people they must obey the Church or they would go to Hell.

Being aware of this concept, we know that in these traditions, as in many other traditions, the gods and divine entities were stars in the heavens. The gods are the Sun, the Moon, planets, comets, stars, groups of stars and constellations, mechanisms that take place in the heavens, which bring life on Earth, such as light, rain or the tides, but which may periodically bring destruction to the earth, as with the Universal Deluge.

The Great Flood is another tradition that is widespread throughout the world: from the Aboriginals to the Chinese, from the Mesopotamians to the Egyptians, from the Scandinavians to the Inuit, from the North American Indians to the Maya. All these legends and myths have been well documented by Alexander and Edith Tollmann.

In these traditions, we note another distinctive feature: the Great Flood was initiated by the god or gods. So there is a mechanism by which the heavens can decide when a Great Flood takes place on the earth. So the great almighty God in Heaven was a group of heavenly entities, stars, comets etc. that periodically brought death and destruction to the earth. God is a heavenly mechanism.

From this point of view, we understand the four archangels Gabriel, Michael, Raphael and Uriel to represent the four constellations in the four corners – the four guardians – of the firmament.

In this way, old traditions, myths and religious texts become more meaningful, as we know that they are talking about important events on Earth, caused by events taking place in Heaven, where planets and stars are the gods.

The well-known and respected translator of Sumerian texts, Zecharia Sitchin, understood that these traditions of the gods were not just an invented fantasy, but described real cosmic incidents, such as the gods or planets Marduk and Tiamat, whose collision caused the genesis of the Earth; events that, of course, took place long before the existence of humanity. As these events took place before the existence of humanity, who observed these cosmic incidents?

Zecharia Sitchin understood that some unknown, intelligent extra-terrestrial life was responsible. Therefore, if some unknown, intelligent extra-terrestrial life described these cosmic events, maybe there were also some texts in the Sumerian traditions that described this intelligent extra-terrestrial life. That's smart thinking! So Zecharia Sitchin searched for anecdotes about them in the Sumerian traditions, and he thought he had found them with the traditions of Enki and Enlil. But he misunderstood, since Enki and Enlil were just like the Egyptian Seth and Horus, representatives of the Northern and Southern Hemispheres, through which the concept of duality is explained.

The gods, the Anunnaki, were not aliens, but stars, planets and constellations, which came from Nibiru, which is not a planet, but represents the heavens. These Anunnaki were the heavenly stars in the sky, Nibiru, and the legends about the Anunnaki described events that took place in Heaven.

In the late Sumerian texts, gods, stars and constellations were collectively known by one name: Elohim. Elohim means "the one god", but refers to all stars and constellations. However, this Elohim is not just a simple reference to all gods, but means something more, as it is this god who decided that the Great Flood would take place on the earth. Therefore, Elohim is more than just a collective name. Elohim refers to a mechanism in the heavens that can cause great disasters on the earth at certain times. The god consisting of the Sun, the Moon and all objects above in the sky gives life on Earth through sunshine, rain etc., but can also destroy the Earth. So Elohim actually refers to this heavenly mechanism in which all planets, stars and constellations are the members, or gods.

From these old Sumerian traditions came the oldest texts in the Old Testament of the Bible. It's ironic that the Sumerian traditions are presumed to be legends while the Christian texts of the Old Testament, derived from them, are considered holy and sacred. In the Bible, the name Elohim has simply been replaced by the name Yahweh, though the texts are mostly identical. The God of the Bible was actually not called Yahweh at first, but referred to only using the four letters Y, H, W and H. In order to pronounce these four letters, two vowels (A and E) were inserted, and so the four letters became the word Yahweh, though it was said that this name should not be spoken. These four letters Y, H, W and H referred to the four corners, or cardinal points, of the heavens. Yahweh in the Bible therefore referred to the whole firmament, again with this mystical heavenly mechanism that brings life but can also destroy the Earth. Yahweh was the group of stars and constellations and other bodies in the sky, which can periodically cause great floods on Earth.

Mauro Biglino, who translated 18 complete original Old Testament texts, shows that other historical texts were added to the authentic ancient texts. In the added texts, he could distinguish more than thirty different real individuals to whom the name of Yahweh was given. Therefore, the decisions of Yahweh in these texts sometimes came from the governor, other times from a battle chief, and occasionally from other people. The confusion came about because powerful people stole the identity of Yahweh in order to appear more powerful and to legitimate their decisions. As a result, the significance of the ancient traditions in the Old Testament became more and more unclear.

In a similar way, the Egyptian pharaoh Akhenaten tried to unify the rich world of Egyptian gods into one collective god, Aten, in order to give more value to this one heavenly mechanism that gives life but can also destroy the earth. However, the Egyptians had become so attached to the sun god Amun and all the other Egyptian gods that it was difficult to order these indoctrinated minds to simply change and ignore their gods in favour of just one god, Aten. In fact, after the death of Akhenaten, his son Tutankhaten was forced, under pressure from the most influential people in Egypt, to reform the monotheistic religion back into the extensive system of many Egyptian gods, with their sun god Amun. As a result of this reformation from the cult of Aten into the cult of Amun, the name Tutankhaten became Tutankhamun.

The biggest concentration of worshippers in the Old Testament developed in Egypt, since it was the country of wealth and security. At that time, despite their hopes and dreams, the Israelites led a miserable existence working as slaves to the Egyptians. Eventually, certain events convinced them of a divine decision that the time had come to escape to a better place. This took place under the guidance of Moses. During this escape, some believers wanted to once again worship a particular god, Taurus, referring to the constellation corresponding to the era in which they were living. This made Moses angry, as he believed they should not worship individual gods but only the universal sky god of the mechanism that controls life and death on Earth. He did not want them to forget this important belief.

Moreover, during this escape, Moses realised that he needed to instil discipline within this large group of people. Rules or laws were necessary in order for the group to complete its journey. Consequently, he invented the Ten Commandments and dedicated them to Yahweh to ensure they would be more respected. Probably unaware of the consequences of this action, Moses transformed the nature of God from a heavenly mechanism into a divine entity with its own consciousness who rules over mankind.

From that moment until the birth of Jesus, this belief or devotion fragmented into a number of different religions, resulting in the formation of groups such as the Pharisees, the Corinthians, the Nazarenes etc. Jesus was born during the transition from the Age of Aries to the Age of Pisces. These astrological ages were observed by looking to the eastern horizon, to the three kings or stars in the Orion Belt. That's why it is written that three kings came from the east when Jesus was born, and that's why the Christians, the disciples of Jesus, were known as the fishes, called to the new Age of Pisces. Jesus also referred to the eastern horizon when he said that a new age, a new empire, would reappear in the sign of Aquarius, and so the day of the resurrection of Jesus remained connected with the name "Easter".

Jesus was born in Bethlehem to a father and mother from two different religions. While Mary, the mother of Jesus from Nazareth, was a Nazarene, Joseph, his father, was a Pharisee. Because of the shame associated with his father belonging to another religion, his mother's family could not legally accept Joseph as the father. So it was said that Jesus had no natural father, and that he was born by God's will.

However, as Jesus knew both religions very well, he was aware of the common knowledge of the divine cross in Heaven that decides Earth's destiny. More importantly, he believed that the different religions should unite again and that their followers should respect one another rather than continue fighting. Because of this belief, this mythical man became a symbol. Although he was sarcastically called the king of all regional religions, he gave his life to bring peace, and in the name of the almighty God, he tried to educate people to love and respect one another.

This man became the founder of Christianity. Nowadays, the Church places the highest value on peace, solidarity, love and respect. During the Middle Ages, however, it lost all control, killing innocents in holy wars, burning tens of thousands of women alive as witches, and torturing and killing hundreds of thousands of people such as the Cathars in the South of France and the famous Templars, while gathering the richest patrimony in the world.

During the time of the Romans, there were many different versions of the Bible, to which the practical Romans liked to add their own interpretations and realistic values. Finally, in the fourth century, Pope Gregorius put an end to this chaos and decided which texts should or should not be included in the Bible and which interpretations should be given to it.

And so the Vetus Latina was born. After this, further rewritings and reinterpretations took place until Pope Damasus I established the Vulgate, which can be considered the modern Bible.

By understanding the history of the biblical texts, it becomes clear that in the oldest texts of the Old Testament, God referred to a certain heavenly mechanism that was able to wreak disaster on the whole earth at long intervals.

We know, therefore, that in the oldest legends and traditions, myths and beliefs, the roles were often performed by planets, stars, constellations and other celestial bodies. In order to discover the real meaning of these texts and the real events that happened, we will analyse these texts carefully in the chapters that follow.

CHAPTER 2
WHICH GODS WERE THE MOST IMPORTANT
TO WORSHIP?

In Chapter 1, we saw that in the old legends and traditions, myths and religious beliefs, gods were planets and stars, the Moon and the Sun, comets, constellations and other celestial bodies. However, we noticed that these divine entities in the sky were associated with a mystical mechanism that could decide when to bring death upon the earth. This "one almighty god" mechanism is the most important concept. We will therefore investigate it to find out more.

When we analyse the traditions in more depth, it is surprising to see the important role given to the zodiac in these legends and traditions. The zodiac is nothing more than a belt of constellations around our planet, which seemingly has no influence on it. So why did our ancestors all over the world worship a zodiac? The Egyptians and Sumerians, for instance, divided their zodiac into twelve signs or constellations. These are the signs that are still used in our modern age, even though some of the signs may have been replaced. In China, other signs were used for the zodiac. Some groups, like the Maya, had more than twelve signs, although the zodiac with twelve signs is most common.

The Christian church wanted to eliminate this worship and knowledge and built temples, churches and cathedrals on top of these former holy places. Sometimes it was difficult to erase these beliefs, so the church slyly substituted symbols for theirs, or gave a Christian meaning to old symbols so that the old belief would vanish. Of course, in this way, the power of the Church grew. For the twelve signs of the zodiac, they substituted the twelve Stations of the Cross: twelve scenes of the crucifixion of Jesus. And in the same way, they substituted the meaning of the highest symbol: the holy cross, such as the Celtic cross, Greek cross or Egyptian Ankh cross, dedicating it to the death of Jesus, even though history tells us that Jesus was killed not on a cross but on a post, as was typical for Roman crucifixions. The holy cross in the sky would decide when death arrives on the earth and when a new age would resurrect. So assigning this meaning to the death and resurrection of Jesus replaced the old meaning in a rather clever way.

What is the significance of the zodiac? During the night, the belt of constellations in the zodiac seems to turn 180 degrees because of the Earth's rotation, and as we can see 180 degrees of the sky on Earth, we see all the signs of the zodiac. Over a period of one year, the signs turn 360 degrees because of the Earth's movement around the Sun. So why would the zodiac be significant for us on Earth?

How did our ancestors observe this zodiac? Let's look again at what Jesus said. He observed the zodiac on the eastern horizon during the spring equinox just before sunrise. He showed his disciples that the Age of Pisces could be seen on the eastern horizon at that moment, just before the rising sun would cause it to fade away. This is interesting. A specific day of the year and one specific moment in that day was chosen to observe which sign had set on the horizon. From traditions and archaeological artefacts, buildings and observatories, it seems that this was a common feature of religious worship throughout the world: every year, they would choose the same moment of the year to observe the position of the stars, to determine which part of the zodiac they were in. These zodiac periods or ages were of the utmost importance and were recorded very carefully. During the Age of Taurus, for instance, the bull represented by the constellation of Taurus was worshipped. Because of this, the Palace of Knossos was decorated with the bull's horns as a symbol of Taurus, from which their sacred bull feasts were also derived. This is why the disciples of Moses worshipped the golden bull. This is why the era of the Christians was the Age of Pisces.

The Egyptians calculated dates according to the zodiac period. For this reason, they used the symbol of the Djed, which symbolised a pillar that supported the firmament. A Djed or pillar without any cross bars represented the first period of a zodiac, which was usually referred to as the first sign of the zodiac. The ages of zodiac signs are not all the same length. Some signs have longer time intervals than others, and the space between two signs is never the same. We can only guess whether the Djed periods were identical to the zodiac sign periods or whether the Djed periods were based on a more accurate mathematical calculation of the precession. A Djed with one cross bar represented the next period in the zodiac: the second sign. A Djed with two cross bars was the third period in the zodiac, and so on until the Djed with five cross bars, which symbolised the sixth period in the zodiac and which can be found in the centre of the Great Pyramid of Cheops. After the sixth period, a half-zodiac was completed, and they restarted from the beginning for the second half-zodiac, once again with a Djed without any cross bars. It was therefore possible to use a Djed to determine the period; according to how many cross bars appeared on the Djed, it was clear from which period the Djed came and to which age of the zodiac the Djed referred. Most of the Djeds that have been discovered have four cross bars, which means that they date from the glorious Egyptian period starting in around 2150 BC and ending in around 1 AD.

However, Djeds have also been found with only three cross bars, dating from the previous age, and on rare occasions Djeds with five cross bars, from the subsequent age, have been discovered.

Fig. 1: Djeds with each 4 cross bars

The Maya observed the zodiac during the winter solstice in order to determine which age they lived in. Other civilisations used the autumn equinox or the summer solstice, though we are most familiar with the civilisations that used the spring equinox for this purpose. Why did they use equinoxes or solstices rather than other days of the year? The answer is that the equinoxes or solstices are days that can be determined precisely within a year, even without a calendar. They were the most convenient days of the year for repeating the zodiac observations accurately.

On the chosen day, some civilisations selected the moment when the sun had just set, but in most cases they used the moment just before the sun rose and caused the light of the stars in the sky to fade away. For this reason, they chose a time that was the same every year to observe the zodiac in the sky and use its position to determine the age of the zodiac.

The same observation direction was chosen every year: often the eastern (sometimes the western) horizon. The horizon line serves as an indicator of the zodiac age. However, there were also civilisations that built observatories, such as Stonehenge, Tihuanaco or the Great Pyramid, in which they constructed observation points. Additionally, other civilisations chose to look straight up into the sky or to the geographical north to determine the age of the zodiac. As a result, the signs of the zodiac differed from civilisation to civilisation, even though they referred to the same ages. For instance, the lion from the Age of Leo referred to the same zodiac age as the Dragon or the winged Snake from other civilisations. Leo was visible on the eastern horizon during the spring equinox just before sunrise while the Dragon was the constellation that appeared in the geographical north during that same period.

Therefore, the interesting question is: "Why did ancient civilisations observe the signs of the zodiac?" The movement of the zodiac belt creates different zodiac ages that last for long periods of time. The zodiac takes 25,776 years to rotate once around the Earth, which is called the precession. During a period of 25,776 years, there are twelve ages represented by the zodiac signs or constellations. Because of the precession movement, ancient civilisations were able to observe the shifting of the zodiac signs on the eastern horizon during the spring equinox at the moment just before sunrise, and so they knew which period of the precession or which age of the zodiac they were living in.

This zodiac cycle or precession cycle was the collective name for all the stars in the sky, which demonstrated this most important mechanism of rotating over a period of 25,776 years, during which time they brought life or could decide to destroy the earth. The precession cycle was almighty, the most important and greatest event in the sky, with the power of life or death, and consequently it was observed carefully and worshipped in ancient buildings, traditions and symbols.

This is rather frightening, however: the zodiac cycle is a precession movement that takes 25,776 years to rotate just once. We should be very surprised by the fact that all of the world's civilisations considered this the most important thing of all: to know which period they were living in within a seemingly insignificant cycle that takes 25,776 years! We should concern ourselves with why so much importance was assigned to it, and why it was observed so accurately throughout the world. In any case, we should wonder why they would observe a cycle of 25,776 years, given that people in those days lived until they were 35 to 40 years old at most: too short for any one person to notice the zodiac moving through the precession cycle during his or her own lifetime.

While the firmament appears to turn once around the Earth every 24 hours, causing the incredible spectacle played out by the Moon and Sun, and while it seems to turn once around the Earth every year, causing the seasons, we apparently think it normal that the turning of the firmament once around the Earth every 25,776 years should be considered the most important, being ascribed the power to control life and death. Nowadays, there is little interest in why this knowledge formed the basis for fervent worship all over the world. Are we really so arrogant, living in our high-tech age, as to claim to possess all wisdom and consider our ancestors to be insignificant or stupid worshippers? If they knew about the 25,776-year precession movement, can we really call them insignificant? How many people today understand this precession movement? How many people today know how to observe this precession movement? If we hadn't read about it, how many people would have known about it or thought about it? In one human lifetime, it is impossible to observe the precession movement. How did all our ancestors, all over the world, obtain this knowledge? And why did it become so important for them?

What is important about such a long cycle? Why is it important to know which period of this cycle we are living in? Do we need to know about certain significant moments within this cycle of 25,776 years? Does something happen at certain moments of this precession cycle or zodiac cycle? And is this the reason why our ancestors accurately observed this long zodiac cycle, ascribing it the power of life and death? What did they say about it? Job 9:9–10 says: "He is the Maker of the Bear and Orion, the Pleiades and the constellations of the south. He performs wonders that cannot be fathomed, miracles that cannot be counted". Job 38:31–33: "Can you bind the chains of the Pleiades? Can you loosen Orion's belt?... Do you know the laws of the heavens? Can you set up God's dominion over the Earth?"

In order to know whether the precession movement can really cause disastrous events on Earth at certain points in its cycle, we need to understand what the precession is. In the next chapter, we will analyse the precession in detail and will find that the reality is very different from what science claims to know about it. Just as the 24-hour rotation causes night and day, and the yearly orbit causes the seasons, so the precession cycle also has an effect on Earth.

CHAPTER 3
THE PRECESSION MOVEMENT IS AN ORBIT
OF OUR SOLAR SYSTEM

In the previous chapters, we concluded that the precession movement represents the most holy and sacred knowledge revered all over the world and ascribed the power to control life and death on the earth.

But what exactly is the precession movement? Because we know it is not the stars that are turning around the Earth, we simplistically assume that it is the Earth that is spinning around. This would mean that the precession cycle can only be caused by the spinning of the Earth. But is this actually the case? Are there no other possibilities? Did we overlook something? Yes, we did!

We might have already had an inkling about this, from the nature of the observations and the duration of one rotation. The 24-hour rotation of the Earth can be easily attributed to the spinning of the Earth around its axis. The yearly turning is caused by the Earth's orbit around the Sun. So in fact it is not a rotation of the Earth but a rotation of the solar system, even though every planet in our solar system has its own timeframe in which it turns once around the Sun. So although we are talking about a rotation of the solar system, each planet has a different period, or timeframe, in which it rotates once around the solar system. So thanks to the Earth's orbit, it rotates around the Sun once in a year, and this means that the zodiac seems to turn around the Earth once in a year.

If we now consider the way in which we observe the precession, we notice that the position of the Earth with respect to the position of the Sun and stars is constantly shifting. So it appears as if our solar system has an orbit in which it takes 25,776 years to complete one rotation. Because of this, the firmament seems to move once around the Earth every 25,776 years, but this is actually caused by the orbit of our solar system, which takes 25,776 years. So the precession movement is not directly caused by the Earth's rotation, but by the orbit of our solar system, of which the Earth forms part.

So, just as the 24-hour rotation can be attributed to the spinning of the Earth, the yearly turning can be attributed to the Earth's orbit, and the 25,776-year turning, or precession cycle, can be attributed to the orbit of our solar system. In addition, there is a 200-million-year turning caused by the rotation of our Milky Way, which moves our solar system at a speed of 250 km/s. But taking a few steps back: because of the precession cycle, or solar system orbit, the sky seems to shift by 50"290966 each year and takes 25,776 years to complete a full rotation.

Because of the solar system's orbit, every planet in our solar system will take 25,776 Earth years to complete one precession cycle. However, some confusion reigns in the scientific world, as the currently accepted viewpoint is that the turning of the sky can only be caused by the Earth and nothing else. So scientists regard the precession as a supplementary rotation of the Earth, while forgetting about the orbit of our solar system, as if it doesn't exist. But it does exist, and this creates a huge contradiction. Science aims to justify the precession as a supplementary rotation of the Earth, which leads to theories about the mutual forces between the planets of our solar system. These forces exist of course, just like the Earth influences the Moon and the Moon influences the Earth. By searching for formulas based on the mutual forces between planets without considering the orbit of our solar system, and including the actual precession movement as a constant, science tends to find results that fit the generally accepted theory for the precession of the planets, though it is not 100% correct, as the actual precession of our solar system has been reduced to an unknown constant. Or in other words: science searches for formulas that prove what it wants to believe, even though the formulas do not fit 100% and the orbit of our solar system has been eliminated as if it doesn't exist.

However, it is scientific knowledge that our solar system is situated 26 light years above the orbital plane of the Milky Way, and that it moves at a speed of 20 km/s to an apex located upwards and towards the centre of the Milky Way. Because the Milky Way is spinning, all its star systems are pushed into a flattened disc in which they fly away from the centre of the Milky Way as a result of the centrifugal force. This means that our solar system should move in a downward direction as it is situated 26 light years above the Milky Way's orbital plane. It should also move outwards, away from the centre of the Milky Way, because of the centrifugal force. However, our solar system does precisely the opposite: rather than moving downwards and outwards, it moves upwards away from the galactic orbital plane and towards the centre, against the centrifugal force. So our solar system's movement within the Milky Way is entirely contradictory. Does this mean it came from outside the Milky Way, and is flying through the Milky Way in order to escape from it again? No, not at all! Our solar system is just one of many star systems that make up our galaxy. Our solar system is located between other star systems and has an orbit between them. This is caused by the interaction with interstellar plasma, which depends on the forces between star systems – as we will explain clearly in the following chapters. Our solar system has an orbit between other star systems because of their mutual forces. So this solar system orbit should be observable on Earth by the sky shifting over a long period of time. However, scientists have completely disregarded the solar system orbit in their observation of the sky's movement. In this respect, science is contradicting itself! However, the observation of the precession movement fits perfectly with our solar system orbit.

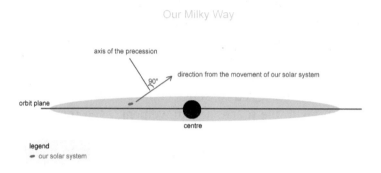

Fig. 2: movement and position of our solar system in our Milky Way

This is even more obvious when we consider the axis, or orbital plane, of the various rotations. The rotational axis of the Earth's 24-hour rotation is inside the Earth, which differs by around 23° from the axis of the solar system. The yearly rotation has an axis that is perpendicular to the Earth's orbit and differs by 23°26' from the Earth's rotational axis. So the yearly rotation has a different axis from the Earth's rotation, and these two different axes cause the different seasons.

The precession axis is also different from the Earth's axis, but is exactly perpendicular to the orbital plane of our solar system. This cannot be a coincidence! The precession axis aligns with the solar system orbit and is totally inconsistent with the Earth's rotation. This clearly shows that the precession depends on the solar system orbit and not the Earth's rotation!

Let's consider an example. If you lie down in a car, and the car slips and starts to spin, it will seem as if everything is turning around you. However, it is actually not you who is turning, but the car you are in. This means that everything will not rotate around your axis, but around the axis of the car, which is perpendicular to the movement or orbital plane of the car. So, if you are lying at an angle of 23°, then the car's axis will differ from your axis by 23°. In the same way, in the precession movement, the Earth's axis is different from the precession axis, which is perpendicular to the orbit of our solar system. And as the solar system has an orbit, the sky should appear to shift in accordance with that orbit – but this is not observed by science. Science attributes other explanations to the precession movement, even though the calculated results do not fit 100%.

So it is clear that the 24-hour rotation of the sky around the Earth is caused by the Earth's rotation. The yearly rotation of the sky around the Earth is caused by the Earth's orbit. The 25,776-year rotation of the sky around the Earth, or precession, is caused by the orbit of the solar system. The daily rotation causes day and night, as well as the tides (thanks to the Moon). The yearly rotation causes the seasons. But what does the precession cause? All the stars in Heaven, the Elohim, which form a turning mechanism together, were considered the most important as they controlled life and death on Earth. Why? What might happen on Earth as a result of the precession?

Pharaoh Khufu (Cheops) excavated the pyramids built by a very ancient civilisation out of the sand, restored them with primitive materials, and dedicated them to himself. Because of this, the pyramids didn't seem to have an entrance, as he closed the entrances during the restoration. He also excavated the Sphinx, which had been totally eroded by the tropical climate and then hidden in the desert sand. The pharaoh decided to replace the eroded head with an image of his own head. During this restoration, important archaeological writings were discovered, which described the precession as well as the reason these buildings were built. The traditions described in detail the twelve periods of the zodiac in the 25,776-year precession cycle and the coming of death and destruction on the earth, followed by a resurrection: a new era. The pharaoh didn't understand the language and his translator could only translate it inadequately. Furthermore, they didn't understand the significance because they lacked astronomical knowledge. Their translations are what we now know as the Egyptian Book of the Dead. As the pharaoh understood that these were very important texts governing life and death, he classified them as sacred prayers and used them during funerals in order to show respect to the deceased and assist them into the afterlife.

As we know that the precession is a solar system orbit that can cause deadly events on Earth, the next few chapters will explore the nature of this destructive mechanism and how and when we can expect such events.

CHAPTER 4
THE CARDINAL POINTS INDICATE THE TIMELINE OF THE PRECESSION CYCLE

In previous chapters, we noted that the precession cycle was the most holy, sacred mechanism worshipped all over the world, and that the precession is actually a solar system orbit. How did our ancestors describe or portray this procession or zodiac cycle?

In the Sumerian civilisation, all the gods – the Elohim or the Anunnaki, all the stars in the sky – came from Nibiru, the heavens, which turned through a precession cycle. The precession cycle was symbolised by a cross that represented the zodiac, and a circle around it that represented the turning of the zodiac. Sometimes wings were attached, symbolising what was above, in the sky. The cross accentuated four points of the zodiac, or four moments of the precession cycle. One leg of the cross represented the first constellation of the zodiac, while the next leg represented the fourth constellation. The next leg of the cross again skipped two constellations and symbolised the seventh constellation of the zodiac. The fourth leg of the cross again moved three constellations forwards, skipping two constellations. After this, the counting restarts with the first constellation. In this way, the holy cross represented the zodiac and, in particular, indicated four opposite constellations or four recurring moments of the precession cycle. The cross with a circle represents all the stars in the sky, which turn in a precession cycle because of the solar system orbit. Unfortunately, Zecharia

Sitchin interpreted this symbol as a planet because he understood that it referred to a location up in the sky, and as a result, he created a very popular fantasy in which the stars, the Anunnaki, came from a planet rather than from the sky and were therefore aliens.

Fig. 3: Christian cross not referring to Jesus

The four legs of the zodiac cross represented the four corners of the world, or the four cardinal points. These cardinal points should not be confused with the four wind directions of the compass: north, south, east and west. The four corners of the world or four cardinal points referred to four opposite constellations in the zodiac, which undergoes a precession movement. Because the zodiac undergoes a precession movement, the four corners of the world continuously shift and make one complete rotation around the Earth every 25,776 years. The cross refers to the four cardinal points, or four opposite constellations of the zodiac, and also indicates four moments during the 25,776-year precession cycle. The holy cross was the most sacred symbol throughout the world. This holy cross with its cardinal points, high up in the sky, controlled life and death, the end of the world and the birth of a new era. Because of this, the precession had to be carefully observed in order to determine when these moments arrived.

When the Sumerian traditions evolved into the origins of the Old Testament, the word Elohim was replaced by the four initial letters of the cardinal points: Y, H, W and H. These letters were later connected with two vowels to form the name Yahweh, though it was believed that the name should not be pronounced with the vowels. Consequently, the holy cross was already the most important symbol before Jesus was crucified.

Fig. 4: The Ankh

The Maya symbolised the precession by their tree of life with four branches. The tree of life supported the firmament and gave life, while the four branches represented the four cardinal points of the zodiac. The Egyptians used the Ankh as their precession symbol and it was believed to give life during the precession cycle. The Ankh became the symbol of life. The Ankh symbolised the holy cross, with the fourth leg replaced by a circle to indicate the movement of the precession. If Egyptians or Sumerians used the circle, they originally intended it to represent the solar system orbit, but this has been misunderstood as a simple reference to the sun. The wings represented what was up in the sky. Therefore, a circle with a constellation of the zodiac on both sides symbolised the era of that constellation during the precession cycle. In this way, a circle with the horns of Taurus referred to the era from around 4500 to 2500 BC.

Fig. 5-8: Sumerian cross

The Celts used a symbol that looked rather like the cross-section of a rolled pancake. This circle referred to the endless precession cycle. The Celts also used a holy cross with a little circle in it, with the four legs of the cross again symbolising the four cardinal points, and the circle representing the movement of the precession cycle. The Northern European symbol, the Swastika, which was unfortunately abused by the Nazis, was another sacred symbol that indicated the precession. The Swastika is a composite symbol made up of two old Scandinavian symbols: one is the Eihwaz, which referred to the tree of life, Yggdrasil, which supported the heavens with its four branches, which are the four cardinal points. The other is the Sowilo, which refers to the sun and the sacred turning mechanism of the precession, the sun's orbit. So both signs together referred to the whole concept of the precession. This holy symbol with the same meaning was also used in Hinduism, Jainism and Buddhism, and can be found in the first Christian catacombs, on Greek and Roman mosaic pavements, and on wooden clogs worn by the Vikings.

Fig. 9: Celtic cross

So the mystery deepens. Why did all ancient civilisations refer to four cardinal points, four opposite constellations of the zodiac, which represented four moments in the precession cycle? The cross indicates four recurring dates during the precession in the past and future, four moments that can be determined by observing the precession. So the zodiac signs are actually like the hours on a clock – a precession clock rather than a normal one. The four cardinal points, the four legs of the holy cross, indicate four particular moments in this precession cycle.

By observing the constellations of the zodiac during the spring equinox at the eastern horizon, just before sunrise, the Sumerian king, the Egyptian pharaoh, the Maya priesthood, the priests of Stonehenge, and Jesus of Nazareth would all be able to determine which point they were at in the precession cycle. It was important to know the timing because at the moments represented by the cardinal points, something in the heavens would decide that a huge event would happen on Earth, and that a new era would emerge, which meant that the old one would be destroyed. Because of this, we can understand how important it was to know the dates indicated by the cardinal points.

In China, the four cardinal points represent four constellations: the Dragon, the Phoenix, the Turtle and the Tiger. In the Beijing Ancient Observatory, there are still a large number of star maps and artefacts showing how the cardinal points were derived. The Dragon refers to a moment almost half a precession ago, between 10,865 and 10,500 BC. The Phoenix refers to a moment around 2023 and 2388 AD. The other two cardinal points represented a moment in the middle of those two and a moment that is around a quarter-precession into the future. Unfortunately, I have still not been able to determine the precise years of the cardinal points. Robert Bauval determines the cardinal point that is half a precession ago as 10,750 BC, basing this on the observatory shafts in the Pyramid of Cheops that indicate the three stars of Orion's Belt.

Fig. 10: The Dragon constellation in the Beijing Ancient Observatory

Why did they use the Dragon as a cardinal point? During the 25,776-year precession, the geographic north shifts according to the stars positioned right above it. The rotational axis of the precession differs by around 23 degrees from the axis of our spinning Earth, and because of this, the geographic north will have different stars above it during the course of the precession movement. Around a half-precession period ago, the geographic north referred to the head of a constellation known as Draco, depicted by a dragon or winged serpent. This cardinal point was very important, as the Sumerians and Egyptians also used two serpents facing each other, with or without a circle, to indicate an important moment that determined life and death. The symbol of two intertwined snakes is still used as a symbol of medicine, which can also determine life and death. In addition, the Maya used the dragon or winged serpent as one of their cardinal points. Every year, at the spring equinox, the shadow of the winged serpent crawls down from the pyramid at Chichen Itza, an event observed by large numbers of tourists.

The Egyptians named the Egyptian cross after the goddess Nut who supported the heavens, while her four children Osiris, Seth, Isis and Nephthys were at the cardinal points, just like the four archangels Michael, Gabriel, Raphael and Uriel from the Old Testament. The four constellations indicated by the four cardinal points were Leo, Aquarius, Taurus and Scorpio. These constellations are not positioned at the geographic north, but around the equator. What is incredible is that they refer to the same moments as the cardinal points in Chinese astrology. They correspond to the same dates during the precession. Leo refers to a point between 10,865 and 10,500 BC, Aquarius to a date between 2023 and 2388 AD, and the other two a quarter-precession before and after. The Egyptians depicted these cardinal points as sphinxes, a fusion of Leo and Aquarius. The sphinxes were the guardians of the cardinal points of the precession. The Mesopotamians combined the same cardinal points of Leo, Aquarius, Taurus and a bird in place of Scorpio, which resulted in the mythological monsters, the Cherubs, with the body of a lion, the head of the water bearer (Aquarius), the legs of a bull and the wings of a bird. The Cherubs were the guardians of the Ark of the Covenant. The Cherubs are actually derived from the Sumerian karibu, which guarded the tree of life that supported the sky, which turned according to the precession. They were literally the fusion of the four cardinal points, referring to around 10,865–10,500 BC, 2023–2388 AD, a quarter-precession before and a quarter-precession after. In the Bible, the cherubs were the angels that guarded the Garden of Eden, in which stood the Tree of Life with a large number of apples, representing stars.

Fig. 11: Cherub – Fig. 12: Roman sphinx

Fig. 13: Orthodox Cherub

So not only was the holy cross the most important symbol in the whole world, the cardinal points in all ancient civilisations also referred to exactly the same moments during the precession cycle. For instance, the European religion of Mithraism referred to the four cardinal points: the snake (representing the winged serpent), the bull, the scorpion and the dog, which represented the Little Bear – the same cardinal point as Aquarius but using a North Pole orientation. It can no longer be a coincidence. These cardinal points, these points of the precession cycle, must have been very important.

When Adam and Eve were in Eden under the Tree of Life, the cardinal point of the Snake arrived, and YHWH became angry and suddenly changed the climate: it became colder and Adam and Eve had to clothe themselves. In the brutal Dark Ages, the Pope didn't understand its meaning and therefore pointed to the woman as the reason for this terrible event, in order to make women subordinate to men, as they believed women to be of little value. Although in this modern age, we no longer practise this sort of discrimination, we still want to understand what exactly happened at the moment corresponding to the cardinal point. We will discover this in the coming chapters.

CHAPTER 5
THE DUALITY: CONSTANTLY RECURRING HALF-PRECESSION PERIODS, SEPARATED BY A PRECESSION DISASTER

In previous chapters, we learned that the cardinal points stand for historic and future dates within the timeframe of the precession, and that on those dates, highly significant events happen on Earth. In this chapter, we will discover what the ancient civilisations said about these events.

As mentioned in a previous chapter, the Egyptians symbolised the different ages of the precession cycle with constellations and they counted these ages by means of a Djed. The zodiac sign eras don't have identical time periods, so we cannot be sure whether the Djed periods were identical to the zodiac sign periods or used a more accurate mathematical calculation of the precession. A Djed without any cross bars represented the first sign or age of the zodiac. In Ancient Egypt, this counting started between 10,865 and 10,500 BC at the end of the Age of Leo. The second age of the zodiac was symbolised by a Djed with one cross bar. In this way, every subsequent age of the zodiac had a Djed with one more cross bar, until the sixth age or sign of the zodiac, represented by a Djed with five cross bars. After the sixth age, having passed through a half-precession cycle, the counting restarts at around 2023–2388 AD in the cardinal point of Aquarius, seemingly indicating that there will be a huge change resulting in a new great era of six signs, just as happened at the start of the half-precession period in the sign of Leo. In other words, the Egyptians counted half-precession periods of 12,888 years, divided into cardinal points. So at two of the four cardinal points, something happens to divide the precession period of 25,776 years into two great eras or half-precession periods. These half-precession periods were designated in ancient times as world years, great eras or world empires, and are described in many traditions all over the world. Jesus also revealed that in the cardinal point of Aquarius, a new era or empire would be born. The two cardinal points that separate the half-precession periods are Leo (or the Dragon or winged serpent) and Aquarius (or the Phoenix). The Menorah, a religious candelabrum with seven branches used in Judaism, originates in this concept of a world year, represented by seven branches that divide six ages or signs of the zodiac, symbolising a half-precession period or world empire.

Because of this, ancient civilisations divided the gods or stars and constellations in the sky into two groups. In Sumer, there were the star gods under the supervision of Enki on one hand, and those ruled by Enlil on the other. In each long period, corresponding to a half-precession period, one of the two is in power. One group is situated above or in the north; the other half is below or in the south. Every 12,888 years, there is an exchange of power. Or in other words, in one world year or great era, one of the two groups of stars is above, in the north, and the other below. In the next half-precession period, the other half is located above, in the north, while the first group is exiled below. The Egyptians also had the same traditions regarding the duality of north and south, represented by the gods Osiris and Seth, in which the transition of power from one to the other between these great eras caused great disruption on Earth. Even in the Catholic religion, this duality is found in the concepts of Heaven and Hell. In the Book of Revelations (12:7–12):

Michael, one of the archangels, is fighting against the precession dragon: "Then war broke out in heaven. Michael and his angels fought against the dragon, and the dragon and his angels fought back. But he was not strong enough, and they lost their place in heaven." Half of the angels or stars, the losers, were sent down to Hell by YHWH for a period of around 10,000 years – more precisely, 12,888 years – after which they were allowed back into Heaven. During this war of the angels in the sky, the earth was almost destroyed by the Great Flood.

Fig. 14: 4 constellations of the cardinal points and 4 archangels on the ceiling of a Christian church

There is a beautiful allegory about duality that can be found in many old civilisations: the Maya, the Egyptians, the Hindus etc. In this allegory of the fire gimlet, they describe a Djed, the pillar or tree of life, which stands on the Earth and supports the sky. Around this pillar or Djed, there is a rope, one end of which is gripped by the god or constellation representing one half-precession period. The other end of the rope is held by the representative god of the other half-precession period. In Egypt, these half-precession periods were represented by Osiris and Seth. Seth and Osiris symbolised the constellations of the Pleiades and Orion respectively. So they both gripped one end of the rope, which stretched from the hand of Seth, around the Djed or life pillar, to the hand of Osiris. For one half-precession period, Seth took control and pulled on the rope in order to turn the Djed along with the sky. Because of the friction of the Djed against the Earth, after being pulled for half a precession cycle, the Earth caught fire. The Earth was burning, and water was poured on the fire in order to extinguish it, which represented the Great Flood on Earth. A great flood of water was unleashed on the burning Earth. Seth could not pull anymore, as the end of the rope held by Osiris was almost touching the Djed. So now it was Osiris' turn to pull on the rope for the next half-precession period of 12,888 years. Because of this, the Djed and the sky were turning in opposite directions. After this half-precession period, the Earth caught fire again and had to be extinguished with water. Seth and Osiris kept repeating this every half-precession.

Fig. 15, 16, 17: the precession cycle, depicted in the allegory as two gods with a fire gimlet

This allegory suggested that the firmament of stars turned in different directions each half-precession period. At the cardinal points between these half-precession periods, there is always a gigantic global disaster involving fire and flood; specifically, this happened around 10,865–10,500 BC and 2023–2388 AD. This seems almost like science fiction, but this theory was found in all ancient religions and knowledge all over the world. It was this knowledge that was diligently worshipped and observed, narrated and written down, depicted with symbols on the greatest temples and pyramids so that it could never be lost and so that descendants would be able to prepare themselves.

This was symbolised in the famous Sun Stone of the Aztecs. It represents the precession or zodiac with twenty zodiac signs, four cardinal points and four intercardinal points. Half of the zodiac turns in one direction, while the other half of the zodiac moves in the opposite direction. During the transition at the moment represented by the cardinal point of the feathered serpent or Dragon, there are earthquakes, huge floods, fire, volcanic eruptions and hurricanes that spare nobody. In Hamlet's Mill, the precession movement is compared to a water wheel with one broken tooth. Every time the precession reaches the broken tooth, an enormous disaster of Great Flood proportions comes over the earth.

But how does the firmament of stars changes direction every 12,888 years? The solar system orbit cannot suddenly stop and start to move in the opposite direction. This is against the laws of physics. Yet we know that the northern stars, gods or angels move to the south after 12,888 years. In the Northern Hemisphere, the northern stars disappear out of view and go below, down to Hell. The southern stars suddenly appear in the sky in Earth's Northern Hemisphere for a half-precession period. This is only possible if the Earth turns upside down. In other words, the Earth

Fig. 18: The Aztec Sunstone

makes a half-rotation so that north and south change place. At the moments represented by the specific cardinal points between two half-precession periods, the Earth will turn upside down. The northern sky will be visible from the south and the southern sky will be visible from the north. This sudden turning of the Earth will obviously cause volcanic eruptions, earthquakes, hurricanes, large tsunamis and great floods. This explains the unexpectedly abrupt movements of the stars, which was imagined to be a war between the gods and angels in Heaven, in which one half was suddenly sent down to Hell, out of view, for a period of 12,888 years in which the resurrected southern stars reigned over the Northern Hemisphere. This precession disaster at the cardinal point when the Earth suddenly turns upside down explains the fact that the firmament of stars seems to move in the opposite direction after the disaster. The Earth's rotation remains intact, but by turning upside down, its rotation with respect to the Moon, the Sun, the planets and the stars seems to be in the opposite direction.

So the precession disaster at the cardinal points between the half-precession periods involves the Earth literally turning upside down, causing the stars in the sky to appear to move suddenly, alongside a great global disaster, after which the stars seem to move in the opposite direction. This means that after the next precession disaster, the Moon will seem to move faster and in the opposite direction, passing twice during a 24-hour period. In the rich traditions of the Egyptian civilisation, it is written that they knew four half-precession periods: two empires or half-precession periods in which the sun rose in the west and set in the east and two periods in which the sun rose in the east.

This global catastrophe cycle was well known to our ancestors. Moreover, the memory is imprinted in our culture. The Egyptian Papyrus Harris, dating from the period of

Ramses III from the 20th dynasty, describes the regularly recurring global catastrophes, in words that could not be chosen more precisely: "This catastrophic cycle is due to an inversion of the magnetic poles, which causes a reversal of the geographic poles". The Papyrus Ipuwer clearly states that the Earth suddenly turned upside down, and complains about the terrible devastations that followed. Papyrus Hermitage 1116B, held in St. Petersburg, again from the second millennium BC, explains this recurrence, over long periods, of the Earth turning upside down, i.e. the precession catastrophe. There are other papyrus scrolls giving similar indications, such as the Papyrus Leiden, or even ritual manuscripts like the Great Magical Papyrus of Paris, which says in its text: "Dear guardians of Pierno, you holy and strong youth, who on command reverse the spinning axis of Heavens' wheel, and unleash thunder and lightning, earthquakes and flashes."

A great number of authors of the Greek civilisation also expressed this cataclysm in accurate terms. For instance, Sophocles speaks in his historical drama about the sun rising in the east instead of the west, as a consequence of the reversal of the poles. Euripides writes in his Electra that the Earth turned around, causing the sun to slide suddenly in another direction. After this event, the stars and the sun continued turning, but in the opposite direction. And even the most respected Romans did not ignore this cataclysm. Seneca wrote in his work Trieste: "Have we, people, deserved this, that the sky should want to destroy us by reversing its poles?" Caius Julius Solinus from the third century AD writes clearly that the Egyptian civilisation was convinced that the sun once rose where it now sets.

Heraclitus from Ephesus (540–475 BC), a representative of the Ionic School, mentioned a period of 10,000 years before the return of these cosmic disasters. And, in fact, this is not a bad estimate! Plato (427–347 BC), a student of Socrates in Athens, also reports on this periodically recurring destruction of the Earth by fire and flood caused by the planets and stars! He particularly emphasised the importance of the position of the stars...! In his Politicus, he says of the recurring disaster: "I mean: the change in the rising and setting of the sun and the other heavenly bodies. Before the catastrophe, they used to set in the quarter where they now rise, and used to rise where they now set." He then went on, assuming that the universe turned around the Earth and not the other way round: "At certain periods the universe has its present circular motion, and at other periods it revolves in the reverse direction. Of all the changes which take place in the heavens this reversal is the greatest and most complete." There were other scientists, too, like Aristotle (384–322 BC), who warned in his Meteorologica of these disasters ravaging the Earth at regular, albeit long, intervals. While we respect the value of the works of all these great scientists, their explanations of the catastrophic cycle are not accepted and dismissed as nonsense. Is it arrogance with respect to ancient people or is it because we cannot accept that we are in such a dangerous position?

This timeframe for the regularly recurring destruction of the world is reflected in the widespread concept of the world year often spoken of in olden times. The world year is the period of time between the eternally recurring, enormous global catastrophes, which lasted for 12,000 years according to the Persians and the Etrurians and 12,924 years according to Cicero, a mere 36 years' difference from the estimated length of our half-precession!!! Cicero was a reporter of true political and historical events. He had no time for fairy tales. So can we ignore this purely descriptive account of a historical fact? With this in mind, the 18th chapter in the book of Enoch, in which an angel is guiding Enoch through the heavenly landscape, becomes somewhat clearer. He shows Enoch the four corners of the world and says to him: "The travelling stars that you see have broken God's commandments. One day, they did not rise at their allotted times. And God was upset and banished them for 10,000 years until the time came to redeem their sin."

Other myths are also made clearer. The great Saturn, also called Father Time, took drastic measures to separate the Ancestors of Earth, the older stars or northern stars, from the younger generation or southern stars. Here, the separation refers to the global disaster. The Children of Heaven pushed the sun out of its place and it began to move. Heaven was no longer in its allotted position and nothing – days, months, years, the rising and setting of stars – would go back into its rightful place. The equinox points were pushed away. The Children of Heaven have separated from the Ancestors, and now the time machine is rolling forward, creating with every new era "a new heaven and a new earth", as it is literally described in the words of the traditions.

Every half-precession period of 12,888 years, the Earth rotates in the opposite direction, because it turns upside down after every half-precession cycle. While it turns upside down, which last happened between 10,865 and 10,500 BC, a cataclysmic global disaster occurs, destroying almost everything and everyone: volcanic eruptions, earthquakes, hurricanes, tsunamis and great floods. After the Earth has turned upside down, the southern stars will be visible in the Northern Hemisphere.

A Chinese version of the legend mentions a cosmic incident that would result in a reordering of the planets in our solar system: "The Earth fell to pieces and the waters in it spurted out and flooded the Earth... the planets changed orbit and the magnificent balance between the Universe and Nature was disturbed." In a myth passed down orally among the Hopi Indians, the beginning of our age is described as follows: "The first world was destroyed because the people misbehaved. The second world ended when the Earth's axis toppled over, covering everything with ice, because their land moved closer to the polar region during this turnover, somewhere between 23,753 and 23,388 BC. The third world ended with a global flood between around 10,865 and 10,500 BC. The current world is the fourth. Its destiny depends on whether the inhabitants act in harmony with the Creator's plan." But YHWH's plan has been forgotten by Earth's inhabitants. In other myths, the Hopi Indians confirmed clearly that the serpent (which represents one of the two crucial cardinal points in the precession cycle) turned the world upside down, and water spouted up through the "kivas". The Pawnee Indians of America preserved similar memories of a remote catastrophe when the northern pole star and southern pole star changed places. The Inuit of Greenland informed early missionaries that several ages ago, the Earth turned upside down, causing an enormous displacement of the world's oceans.

On the same note, the Babylonian epic Erra says: "The natural laws of heaven and earth were thrown out of balance, and the stars in the sky, the residences of the heavenly gods, moved and did not return to their original place." This is also hinted at in the book of Job: "There were many problems in the days of Job... The sun did not behave normally. It shook the earth out of its place, and the earth pillars trembled... and those who commanded the sun did not let it rise..." A little further on we read: "Did you command the sun to rise from another horizon?" Mayan's legends tell us the following: "... it was not known where the sun would shine. They looked in all directions, but they could not tell where the sun would rise. Some thought it would happen in the north, and they cast their eyes in that direction. Others thought in the south. In fact, their thoughts wandered in all directions, because the morning dawned from every side. Some, however, had focused their attention on the east, and said the sun would rise there. It was their opinion that finally turned out to be correct." The Cashinahua, an indigenous people of Brazil, described the disaster in a different way: "The lightning flashed and the thunder roared terribly and everyone was scared... Heaven and Earth changed places."

Here is one of the best-known myths from the time of the ancient Greeks. The story is about Phaeton. His parents were the sun-god Helios and the Earth woman Clymene. Because Phaeton wanted to know if he was truly of godly origin, he visited his father Helios in his castle. In answer to the question of whether Helios was truly his father, Helios confirmed that he was, assuring Phaeton that he would never deny his son. To remove any doubt, Phaeton was granted a wish and Helios would grant it. Phaeton wanted to drive his father's sun-chariot, drawn by fiery horses, which Helios drove around the skies every day. Helios did not want to break his promise, but tried to dissuade his son from the plan. Nevertheless, when dawn broke and the last stars faded away, the son began his heavenly ride in his father's sun-chariot. His father advised him not to take too low a path, nor to climb too high, but to stay in the middle. The horses stormed forwards and quickly realised that the driver was inexperienced, and this very soon made them veer off the usual path. Sometimes they hit the stars and not one of the constellations remained in its place. Then they flew over the earth again, turning it into a blazing sea of fire. The god Zeus looked upon the scene with great sorrow and decided to put an end to it by bringing down the chariot with one of his thunderbolts. Phaeton crashed down in the river Eridanus. In the dialogue "Critias" by Plato, Solon says that this is not just a story, but reflects a true event, told through a story so that it would survive better. The importance of it was under-lined by the Greek poet Nonnus who wrote 21,000 verses on the subject! "There was tumult in the sky shaking the joints of the immovable universe: the very axle bent which runs through the middle of the revolving heavens. Libyan Atlas (= the god who held up the heavens) could hardly support the self-rolling firmament of stars, as he rested on his knees with bowed back under this greater burden."

Herodotus tells of his conversations with the Egyptian priests somewhere in the second half of the fifth century BC. The Egyptian priests assured him that "in the famous time of the Egyptians, the sun rose four times on the opposite side to where it normally rose. Twice it rose where it now sets and twice it rose where it rises now." Pomponius Mela, a Roman author from the first century, also wrote: "The Egyptians are proud of the fact that they are the most ancient people in the world. In their authentic traditions, which you can read be-cause they still exist, it is written that the course of the stars has changed four times, and that the sun twice set in the area of the sky where it rises today." Another example is taken from the book "Le livre de l'au-delà de la vie" by Albert Slosman. He succeeded in providing a better translation of the Egyptian Book of the Dead, which other translators had encountered more difficulties with because the hieroglyph-ic descriptions of recurring world catastrophes did not fit in with modern concepts. It describes the kind of heavenly events that took place during the fall of Atlantis.

I am the Almighty, the First, the Creator of heaven and earth; I am the designer of human bodies

And supplier of the Spiritual Parts. I have placed the sun on a new horizon as a sign of benevolence and as proof of the Alliance.

Explanation: He has exalted the rising of the sun to a new horizon to make the new earth a reality.

It suddenly becomes clear why all ancient peoples anxiously kept an eye on the sky. Astronomy was the key to determining the time of the terrible recurring catastrophe.

To our ancestors, astronomy seemed to be the highest priority. They were even able to determine the intersections in

the precession. Various authors have given thousands of examples in which the position of the sky, so important to the ancient peoples, was kept up to date, described and related

to the recurring cataclysms. Even temples and pyramids, spread throughout the world and aligned with constellations and the solstices, are evidence of this. The precession movement was very important. This is the reason for the origin of the zodiac, which corresponds to the precession. This is why the zodiac was so important in all ancient civilisations. In many ancient civilisations, there have even been descriptions of what the world was like before the catastrophe, based on the previous skies. I am referring, for instance, to the tomb of Senmut or Senenmut, the architect of Queen Hatshepsut. The ceiling indisputably shows a sky where the north is the south and the south is north, and on which the stars turn from the west to the east. To make it even more unambiguous, above this description and drawings, the current movement of the stars is indicated.

In Job 9:9–10 it says: "who made the Bear and Orion,

the Pleiades and the chambers of the South, who does great things beyond searching out, and marvellous things beyond number." Job 38:31–33 tells us: "Can you bind the chains of the Pleiades or loose the cords of Orion? Do you know the ordinances of the heavens? Can you establish their rule on the earth?" Amos 5:8–9 states: "He who made the Pleiades and Orion, and turns deep darkness into the morning and darkens the day into night, who calls for the waters of the sea and pours them out on the surface of the earth – the Lord is his name; who makes destruction flash forth against the strong, so that destruction comes upon the fortress."

In the next chapter we will analyse the role of Hathor in this precession event.

CHAPTER 6
HATHOR, THE GODDESS THAT REPRESENTS THE PRECESSION EVENTS

In the previous chapter, we saw that ancient civilisations all over the world ascribed great religious importance to world years or great eras, which are half-precession periods of 12,888 years, separated by huge global disasters in which the Earth turns upside down. This explains the reason why they took great care to observe the zodiac in the precession cycle.

My favourite allegory is that of the Egyptian goddess Hathor, who has parallels in other religions, such as Ninmah or Ninhursag from the Sumerian period. Hathor was the goddess who represented the whole precession event, and because of this the whole precession cycle was written down in detail in her Denderah Temple. Modern science estimates that the Temple of Hathor at Denderah was built around 81–96 AD. However, it seems that during that period there was actually a "restoration" by the Romans, because there is a reference to the temple in the ancient text of the 4th dynasty between 2613 and 2494 BC) (See "The Dawn of Astronomy", Sir Norman Lockyer.)

Fig. 19: Hathor as depicted in tombs

Hathor has often been represented with the ears of a cow, or even as a cow. She emphasised the female characteristics of nourishment, feeding one half of the precession cycle with one breast and, with the other, the remaining 12,888 years, during which the world is in a reversed position. Coincidentally, one group of zodiac signs refers to a half-precession period that ended around 10,865–10,500 BC, and the other half is upside down, referring to a period that ended around 2023–2388 AD. This allegory shows clearly that these periods were separated: Hathor gave life at the start of a half-precession period. Then the Earth turned upside down, and she gave life again at the start of the next half-precession period. This reversed position in the second half-precession period has to be interpreted literally, since in her temple, there is a zodiac calendar in which the zodiac signs corresponding to one half-precession period appear upside down.

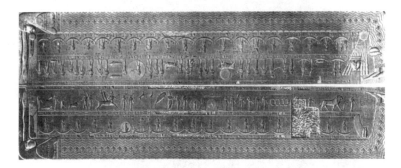

Fig. 20: the zodiac in the temple of Hathor at Denderah

This is why Hathor took on a destructive quality between these half-precession periods. During that time, she was held responsible for the precession disaster. This was written in the book of the Holy Cow, which was discovered in the tomb of Tutankhamun and other Theban tombs. In this story, Hathor is sent by Ra to punish mankind. In the form of a lioness, like the zodiac sign of the "Lion" (Leo), she devastated mankind so terribly that Ra, frightened, sent Shu and Thot. This happened around 10,865–10,500 BC in the sign of Leo. This is why, at old monuments, two lions are often constructed on opposite sides, facing in opposite directions: the Earth turned around in the sign of Leo and then came back in the sign of Leo, because the reversal did not change the position of the Earth with respect to the zodiac signs. The difference was, however, that in around 10,865–10,500 BC, the sun stopped rising from the west, but changed and rose from the east. A Coptic papyrus scroll tells us the following in analogy to other legends: "The world flood shall take place when the heart of the 'Lion' (Leo) starts to touch the beginning of the head of the 'Crab' (Cancer)." And so, if you trace a line across the zodiac in the Temple of Hathor from the head of Cancer to the heart of Leo, then it goes right through the cross of cardinal points, and we get a date between 10,865 and 10,500 BC.

Besides the lioness Hathor, the Egyptians had another god who represented the destroyer during the reversal of the Earth. His name is Sekhmet, analogous to the Devil from the Bible. After a half-precession period of 12,888 years, Sekhmet appeared from the south below, just like the Devil who came from Hell, in order to destroy mankind.

In the Temple of Hathor, there is an impressive firmament of stars depicted in bas-relief, in which the zodiac calendar can be recognised. This precession calendar has been wrongly interpreted by historians as a calendar that shows the best time for harvesting, even though there is nothing to support such a theory. This explanation only corroborates our old-fashioned idea that the Ancient Egyptians had rather simplistic minds. It is actually an image of the sky incorporating Egyptian gods who represented constellations. One can also discern the twelve zodiac signs. At the four corners of the world or cardinal points, Hathor is depicted standing upright and supporting the firmament. If you trace a straight line between the straight line of the hair of the two facing Hathor figures, this forms the holy cross of the cardinal points. So the Hathors are positioned at 10,865–10,500 BC, at 2023–2388 AD and at the moments representing a quarter-precession before and after these dates. At the edge of the firmament, there are two small indicators that mean "east" and "west" respectively. This is incredible. This means that this firmament is a precession clock. "East" signifies the eastern horizon where the zodiac was

Fig 21: the zodiac from the temple of Hathor at Denderah

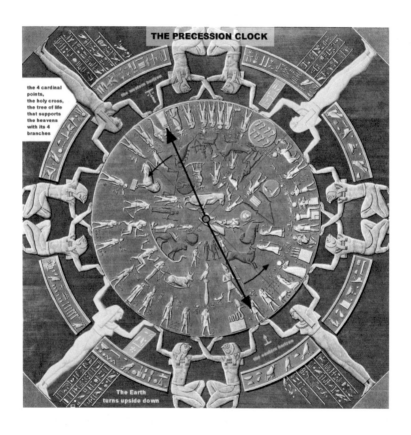

Fig 22: the zodiac from the temple of Hathor at Denderah

observed during the spring solstice, and "west" signifies the western horizon. These two little indicators indicate the year in which this precession clock was created, as they refer precisely to the firmament that was visible in that year on the date of the spring solstice just before sunrise. So the indicators "east" and "west" are rather like the indicators of a precession clock, turning against the direction of the clock. On this calendar from the Temple of Hathor, the indicators refer to a date around 5718 BC.

The Egyptians had a precession clock. The indicators were the two opposite signs "east" and "west", which represented the eastern and western horizons. The numbers on the clock are the constellations in the sky. Because of the precession, the east–west indicator turned slowly in the opposite direction of the clock. In the British Museum in London, a similar precession clock featuring Hathor is on display. Very impressive!

But it doesn't stop here. There are more interesting details on the calendar. It can be seen that the horizontal line from the cardinal point of 10,865–10,500 BC goes right through the heart of Leo, touching the head of Cancer, just as it is mentioned on papyrus scrolls describing the moment of the global disaster. There is also something written next to the arm of the two Hathors, who are standing at the cardinal points when the global disaster takes place. The text literally says: "Here, the Earth turns upside down." It is really marvellous how the Egyptians constructed such a clear and beautiful precession clock, which we didn't understand because we didn't have proper respect for their knowledge.

In fact, other allegories suddenly become easy to understand, such as the story of the scarab beetle. They worshipped the scarab beetle as this insect also represented the precession concept. The scarab puts her eggs in a ball of dung, which symbolises the Earth. In this way, the scarab brings life on Earth. She rolls the ball in the same way as the turning of the precession takes place on Earth. But after one half-precession cycle, a global disaster takes place. After a while, the ball of dung opens to allow the new-born beetles to emerge. It's a nice allegory for a horrifying event. As the construction date on the calendar is around 5718 BC, we can see that this Egyptian knowledge derives from a period long before the Egyptian civilisation that we know and which began around 3,000 years later. This means that the knowledge declined and was no longer fully understood in the Egyptian civilisation that lasted from the third to the first millennium BC. We saw in a previous chapter that the Book of the Dead describes the precession cycle through its twelve zodiac signs or zodiac ages. When Khufu discovered these texts while restoring the pyramids, he understood that the content of these texts must have had enormous value, though he didn't understand their true meaning. Because the texts talked about death and resurrection, he thought they were talking about people: specifically, about death and resurrection in the afterlife. So he introduced the translation of the texts as prayers at funerals. This is an embarrassing distortion of the truth.

Khufu restored the heavily eroded head of the lion or sphinx in his own image, though he didn't touch the eroded body. The pyramids have features that symbolise the precession, such as shafts that point to a time around 10,865–10,500 BC. Another example is a Djed with five cross bars, placed in the centre of the pyramid and referring to the era before the Earth last turned upside down. In addition, the lower chamber has a flat pavement on the ceiling and rough rocky grey finishing on the floor referring to the reversal of the Earth.

Egyptian stories claim that the pyramids were built by Thot in order to preserve the knowledge of the civilisation and of the global disaster. The Coptic text Akhbar al-zaman by the writer Masoudi, which can be found in Oxford, relates the following: "one of the kings before the flood, built the two great pyramids and ordered the priests to deposit within them the written accounts of their wisdom and acquirements in different arts and sciences, that they should remain on record for the benefit of those who could afterwards comprehend them..." In the east pyramid (the one attributed by modern science to Khufu), the celestial spheres were recorded, along with the figures that represented the stars and planets. The king also recorded the position and the cycles of the stars; and at the same time the history and reports of earlier times, about the times to come and about future events that will happen in Egypt." Another old manuscript, written by Al-Maqrizi, echoes this: "The first pyramid was specially dedicated to history and astronomy." And the Tuhfat al Agaib manuscript says: "The pyramid contains the historical plans or orbits of the stars and their signs or consequences, and the prophecies of future consequences due to the orbits of the stars". Even modern science has had to admit that the shape, position, alignment and dimensions of the pyramid show a correlation with our Earth. The upper chamber, the King's Chamber, is described in the Book of the Dead as "The return of the sunlight from the west". In other words, this is the time when the sun will rise from the western horizon instead of the eastern horizon because of the Earth's reversal.

The Ancient Egyptians called the Sphinx either "the guardian of the atmosphere" or "Hwran-Hor-em-akhet", which means: "Horus of the horizon". On the Inventory Stela from 1000 BC is written: "The place of Hwran-Hor-em-Akhet is on the south of the House of Isis, Mistress of the Pyramid, and on the north of Osiris, Lord of Rostaw... [Khufu, another name for Cheops] restored the statue, all covered in painting, of the Guardian of the Atmosphere, who guides the winds with his gaze." After this follows a description of the restoration.

In the 4th century, the Roman historian Ammianus Marcellinus gave the following advice to treasure hunters in Giza: "there are near the pyramids' underground crevices and winding passages called syrinxes. It appears that those who knew the old rites had prior knowledge that a flood would come, and feared that the memory of these ceremonies might be erased. That is why they cut into the earth in many places with great determination".

The Turin Papyrus from around 4000 to 3000 BC clearly describes the royal dynasty that goes back to around 40,000 BC, and this corresponds to other Egyptian papyruses stating that Egypt has known four great eras or half-precession cycles: two in which the sun rose in the east and two in which it rose in the west. With this in mind, we are in a much better position to understand the words in ancient texts and papyruses.

From ancient Indian writings we know about the existence of a similar calendar. Take for instance the documents of Tulasidasa's Shriramacharitamanasa from the 12th century BC. This calendar consists of various interleaved time periods. There are approximately 71 small Yuga cycles, consisting of 360 years, between the Manu and the Mahabharata, which is almost equal to the precession period. Each precession period was divided into four great Yuga, just like the periods between the four cardinal points. This division demonstrates that the authors of these old documents clearly understood the nature of the precession movement. After each period of two great Yuga, the world cataclysm occurs. After the end of the Kali Yuga, around 22,000 BC, Lemuria and Mu, situated in the south of India, were destroyed. In recent years, impressive remains of buildings have been found below sea level in that area. Ancient Tamil texts say that a cataclysm involving a mythical flood destroyed the cities, which included Tenmaturai, Kapatapuram and Maturai. The latter has been rebuilt. When they wanted to build a dyke structure in Madura Oya, the Norwegian engineers came across an earlier dyke structure in exactly the same place while they were digging, which also happened, rather curiously, at Egypt's Lake Nasser. The Norwegian archaeologist Heyerdahl explained that the structure found in the earth consisted of blocks 10 metres high, in the form of square galleries with brick walls. The dykes were longer than 10 kilometres and diverted floodwater into artificial lakes. After the Treta Yuga, around 10,500 BC, Atlantis and the Indian Rama Empire were destroyed. Two great Yugas after the Treta Yuga takes us to around 2023–2388 AD, which is at least a little frightening.

Since ancient traditions clearly describe that the Earth turns upside down every half-precession cycle and causes a global cataclysm, we want to find out if there is scientific proof of these events, and we will look at this in the next few chapters.

CHAPTER 7
THE MAGNETIC FORCE IN OUR SOLAR SYSTEM INFLUENCES THE EARTH

In previous chapters, we saw that ancient civilisations described the existence of half-precession periods between which the Earth turns upside down. As this statement is far removed from our current scientific ideas, we need to analyse it more scientifically to find out the truth about it. What is the scientific explanation for this? The 24-hour rotation of the Earth causes day and night and – thanks to the Moon – the tides. The yearly orbit of the Earth around the Sun causes winter and summer. The precession orbit of our solar system causes a reversal of the Earth every half-precession period. How can this event be explained scientifically?

To be honest, if we were to analyse this in the way that the scientific world requires, then we would need to produce a document containing thousands and thousands of pages. Because there are so many scientific misunderstandings, we would need to prove these as well. It would be a never-ending bible. This is not our goal. Our goal is to explain, in a concise but logical and scientific way, how and why it is possible that the Earth turns upside down after each half-precession period.

We shall start with gravitational force, which is a scientific misunderstanding. It is a force that is only present in matter with a nucleus – i.e. atoms. Matter without a nucleus, such as electrons, protons and photons, is not subject to gravitational forces. The reason is simple: it is the vibration or pulsing of the nucleus that forces the atom to move. This pulsing movement pushes the atom to the centre of conglomerations of mass. In a small conglomeration, there will be almost no gravitational force. The bigger the conglomeration, the larger the gravitational force. Common collisions can cause heavy matter to push light matter away so that heavy matter goes to the centre while light matter is pushed to the outside of the conglomeration of mass. Photons, dark matter, protons and electrons don't have a nucleus and therefore are not subject to gravitational forces. In photons, dark matter, protons and electrons, there is no pulsing nucleus and so the gravitational motor is missing. Gravitation does not influence their movement. This gives them exceptional characteristics as it means they can move freely between masses. They are influenced by forces other than gravitation. They can be present anywhere. Think, for instance, about lightning, light or electricity. Pure electron plasma shields against gravitation force are likely to form the basis of alien technology, used for building elevators of light or for flying objects that can produce amazing acceleration, sudden and dramatic changes of direction or immediate stops using little energy and without any harmful effects for the crew.

However, we observe that two belts, one made of protons and one of electrons, are found at the outermost layer of the Earth's atmosphere, called the Van Allen belts. The reason for this is that some of the protons and electrons escape from Earth, through collisions with matter, and some remain stuck to the border of the Earth as a result of other forces besides the gravitational force. The nearest belt is the belt made up of protons because they have a greater mass density than electrons even though they are smaller. Electrons consist of photons or dark matter and so their mass density is lower. The electron belt is the Earth's outermost belt. There is no photon or dark matter belt as space consists of dark matter.

Because of the Earth's rotation, both Van Allen belts will flatten out towards the equator. These belts are therefore very thick at the equator and become very thin at the poles. At the equator, they are 36,000 km wide, and only 500 km at the poles. Because of the slow solar wind, known as CME, which moves straight from the Sun to the Earth, the belts will be pushed together on the Sun side of the Earth, while on the other side, the belts will be stretched out. The solar wind is made up of protons, electrons, alpha particles and a few ions, which pass the Earth at a speed of 400 km/s. Through collisions, the Van Allen belts are responsible for repelling the slow solar wind so that the CMEs don't reach the surface of the Earth and wipe out most of its life.

Besides the slow solar wind, there is the fast solar wind, also called CME, which consists of almost the same matter as the slow solar wind. The fast solar wind escapes from a geographical pole of the Sun, makes a large curve through our entire solar system and continues to the other side of the solar hemisphere. These solar winds or CMEs fill up our solar system with solar plasma, which is the material that makes up the solar winds, and the atmosphere created by the solar plasma is called the heliosphere. The fast solar wind arrives at Earth's North Pole at 700 km/s and continues to the South Pole. As mentioned before, the Van Allen belts are very thin at the poles and therefore cannot absorb everything, which allows electrons to penetrate the atmosphere and reach the Earth, penetrate the Earth itself and find their way out at the opposite pole. Because of this, electrical equipment can malfunction in polar areas. This is why pilots stay a certain distance from the magnetic poles. This stream of electrons from the North to the South Pole causes the Earth's nucleus to become magnetized. So we have a permanent, huge magnet at the centre of the Earth.

This concept contradicts current scientific thinking, which

assumes that convection streams of fluid iron in the outermost of the Earth's inner belts are responsible for producing this magnetism. But these scientific assumptions are full of paradoxes: is there actually an outermost inner belt of fluid iron? If various convection streams are responsible for the Earth's magnetism, why don't we have various, changeable magnetic north and south poles on the Earth's surface, in line with the various and continuously changing north and south poles on the Sun's surface, caused by its convection streams? Why do we have only one north-south magnetic direction, despite the fact that convection streams in the two hemispheres turn the opposite way, which would be more likely to suggest a north–south–north or a south–north–south magnetic direction?

The Earth's magnetic direction is not determined by the Earth itself but by the magnetic direction of the fast solar winds in our solar system. Because of this, in order to be in alignment with the fast solar winds, the Earth's magnetic poles should rotate in line with the Earth's rotation, as the geographic poles have an inclination of around 23°26'. We observe that the Earth's magnetic poles rotate every 24 hours, although they do not move in total alignment with the fast solar wind. This is due to the elasticity of the Earth's atmosphere: both magnetic poles – the magnetic pole of the fast solar wind and the corresponding pole of the Earth magnet – are slightly bent by the gas atmosphere of the Earth between the two poles, which means there is insufficient magnetic force to influence the stability of the Earth's rotation. We notice this phenomenon between the poles in the aurora borealis and the aurora australis.

However, if the fast solar winds become more powerful, or if the slow solar winds are able to blow the Van Allen belts further away, or if our atmosphere becomes more rarefied or thin, or the angle between the two poles becomes greater, then this might create enough force to cause the breaking point to be reached, allowing the fast solar wind to push the Earth magnet and make it turn over.

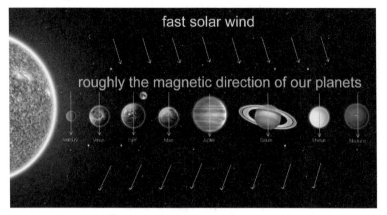

Fig. 23: the link between the fast solar wind and the magnetic direction of the planets

We notice that, by chance, the other planets in the solar system also have the same magnetic direction, corresponding to the fast solar wind within our solar system. This is not surprising from our point of view. Different features on other planets, such as the chemical composition, temperature, gravitational force, nature of the atmosphere or the existence of a nucleus magnet will determine the way in which the planets behave when hit by the solar winds. On all planets except one, the geographic poles are not very different from the magnetic direction of the fast solar wind, which means that geographic and magnetic poles are highly correlated. There is one exception, however: Uranus. Uranus has an inclination that is almost perpendicular to the orbital plane. In fact, Uranus has an inclination of 97°88'. Because of this, Uranus has magnetic poles that deviate from the geographic poles by around 60° in order to align with the magnetic direction of the fast solar winds, rather than with its axis rotation. Moreover, its magnetic poles are not static but move parallel to the equator at the speed of the axis rotation and in the opposite direction. In other words, the magnetic poles always stay in the same position, in alignment with the fast solar wind and independent of the planet itself. Consequently, the direction of the magnetic poles corresponds to the magnetic direction of the fast solar wind, which is obvious from our explanation, but totally inexplicable according to current scientific theories based on convection streams.

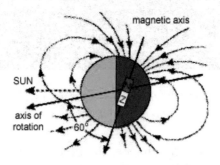

Fig. 24: the magnetic field of Uranus

In summary, we can state that the fast solar wind has caused our planet to become a magnet and that the direction of the magnet is correlated with the magnetic direction of the fast solar wind. In the next chapter, we will see how this magnetic property is the reason why, every half-precession period, the Earth will turn upside down and cause a global disaster.

CHAPTER 8
THE SCIENTIFIC EXPLANATION FOR THE EXISTENCE OF THE HALF-PRECESSION PERIODS SEPARATED BY A GLOBAL DISASTER

In the previous chapters, we discovered that the ancient civilisations knew of the existence of half-precession cycles separated by global apocalypses during which the Earth turns upside down. In order to find a scientific explanation, we considered the fact that our Earth is a huge magnet, magnetised by the fast solar winds and not by the inner convection streams, as is often assumed nowadays. Moreover, this Earth magnet remains aligned with the direction of the fast solar winds. In this chapter, we will see why the statements made by our ancestors were right on the mark.

Since we know that the direction of the fast solar winds determines the magnetic poles of the Earth and the poles of the other planets in our solar system, we need to analyse what the fast solar wind actually is. To start with, we might think of the magnetic field of our Sun. The Sun has a complex and alternating magnetic structure of numerous north and south poles scattered all over the surface, which alternate every 11 years. We call this the 11-year solar cycle. However, this continuously varying magnetic field with its 11-year cycle of alternating poles seems to have hardly any influence on the nature of the solar winds. It does determine the structure of our heliosphere, as well as the direction of the orbits of the planets, and the strength of the solar winds, but not the direction of the solar winds.

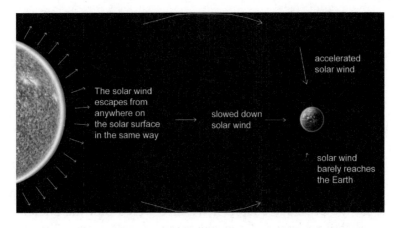

Fig. 25: the solar wind in our Solar System

The solar wind or CME is a stream or flow of protons, electrons, alpha particles and a few ions, which escapes from the surface of the Sun, from any side. Because of the immense heat of one million Kelvin in the corona, protons and electrons reach an average speed of 145 km/s. Some elements, however, attain a speed that is high enough to exceed the escape velocity of 618 km/s. In other words, the solar wind escapes from anywhere on the solar surface without a specific orientation. But the solar winds that escape from the coronal holes in the geographic north of the Sun reach the northern part of the Earth, via a wide curve, at a speed of 700 km/s, which means they appear to have accelerated. This solar wind is called the fast solar wind. The solar wind that escapes at the Sun's equator, or the slow solar wind, seems to have slowed down as it is directed straight at the Earth, passing the Earth at between 300 and 400 km/s. The solar wind that escapes from the Sun's South Pole seems to be neutralised and barely reaches the Earth. Because of this, the Southern Hemisphere of our solar system appears to have no magnetic direction. This has also been measured by the Ulysses probe sent by NASA, whose results astonished scientists and destroyed any existing theories, leaving science with no explanation. But this means that there is something that influences the solar winds or CME after they leave the Sun. We need to find the reason.

Fig. 26: the interaction between the solar wind and the interstellar plasma

The solar winds form the heliosphere of our solar system. The place where the boundaries of our solar system are found is divided into three distinct borders: the termination shock, the heliopause and the bow wave. However, the terminology is far too complex to explain the concept; it could have simply been called the solar system boundary. Why are three different terms in use? The reason is that the solar wind or plasma from our solar system comes into contact with interstellar plasma. At the solar system boundary, the direction and speed of the plasma will be influenced by the interaction of both plasmas and its results are divided by science into three groups according to its net direction. In other words, the collision between our moving solar system and a stream of interstellar plasma will slow down or accelerate the speed of the solar wind at the point of collision, though not to an equal extent everywhere. If there is a difference, even of just one degree, between the orbital plane of our solar system and the directional orbit of the interstellar plasma, then the collisions will not slow down or accelerate the northern and southern solar winds to an equal extent. In other words, the collision with interstellar plasma gives a north–south or a south–north direction to the fast solar wind in our solar system. Of course, if the speed of the northern solar wind increases, and it travels in our heliosphere following a wide curve to the Southern Hemisphere, then the northern solar wind will neutralise the southern solar wind, which has already decelerated as a result of collisions. In the Northern Hemisphere, there is an accelerated magnetic stream of CMEs made up of protons and electrons while in the southern hemisphere, the magnetic direction is neutralised. Collision with interstellar plasma is the reason for the magnetic direction of the fast solar wind travelling into our solar system.

From astronomical observations, such as those described in the official report "Planetophysical State of the Earth and Life", sponsored by the Millennium Group and written by Dr. Alexey N. Dmitriev, we can see that the orbital direction of the interstellar plasma is not identical to the orbital direction of our solar system. Both this and the interaction with interstellar plasma explain why the fast solar wind in our heliosphere has a north–south direction or, in other words, why there is a magnetic north–south direction on Earth. In a nutshell, interstellar plasma is responsible for the magnetic north–south direction on Earth.

What is responsible for the stream of interstellar plasma? This interstellar plasma doesn't move in a straight line – if it did, our galaxy would be emptied. This interstellar plasma, consisting of protons and electrons, is influenced by collisions and/or force fields around it. In other words, the interstellar plasma is imprisoned between star systems and several other phenomena found in our universe, and makes large convection orbits. Protons and electrons turn around between the star systems and other rare force fields. This also immediately explains the orbit of our solar system: it is influenced by the convection stream of interstellar plasma and drifts along with it like a raft on the sea. The convection stream of interstellar plasma causes our solar system to move in a precession orbit. Today's scientists are still wondering about the forces between star systems as they are too far away from one another to be influenced by one another's gravitational force. However, current science ignores the existence of the stream of interstellar plasma, which has already been observed, and does not give any explanation for the movement of our solar system.

So the orbit of the solar system is aligned with the convection stream of interstellar plasma, although its orbital plane is slightly different from the orbital plane of the interstellar plasma, which means that for half the orbit, our solar system will be inclined slightly upwards with respect to the orbital plane of interstellar plasma and for the other half, it will be inclined slightly downwards. So the collisions between the fast solar winds and the interstellar plasma will switch from north to south or vice versa every half-precession orbit. This means that every 12,888 years, the collisions between the interstellar plasma and the solar plasma will cause the northern or the southern solar wind to accelerate in an alternate direction. So the direction of the fast solar wind will continuously alternate between north and south every 12,888 years or every half-precession cycle.

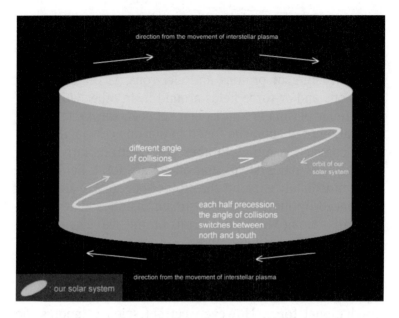

Fig. 27: each half precession cycle, the angle of collisions between the interstellar plasma and the solar plasma switches between north and south

This is problematic, however: if the fast solar wind turns 180° every half-precession cycle, or every 12,888 years, then the magnetic direction on Earth also flips every 12,888 years. Considering that the Earth is a huge, permanent magnet connected with the direction of the fast solar winds, then this permanent Earth magnet needs to rotate 180° when the magnetic direction of the fast solar wind changes, in order to remain harmoniously connected with the magnetic poles. This means that the Earth turns upside down every 12,888 years, just as all ancient civilisations told us. Every 12,888 years the Earth flips 180°. In this way, the geographic North Pole becomes the geographic South Pole, but remains the magnetic north pole. The geographic south becomes the geographic north. This is what all our ancestors regarded as the most holy sacred knowledge, but we didn't understand their words and simply considered them foolish.

The 24-hour rotation brings day and night. The yearly orbit brings winter and summer. The 25,776-year precession orbit brings alternating magnetic poles. The Earth turns upside down every 12,888 years.

Winter and summer are caused by the difference in inclination between the Earth's axis and the axis perpendicular to the Earth's orbit. The alternating magnetic poles are caused by the difference in inclination between the orbit of our solar system and the orbit of the interstellar plasma.

So we can be satisfied that ancient civilisations described it and science can prove it, but is there any geographical proof? Much more than you can imagine. We will cover this in the next few chapters.

CHAPTER 9
THE 11,000-YEAR SOLAR CYCLE

From previous chapters, we know about the existence of half-precession cycles of 12,888 years, after which the Earth turns upside down. If this is true, geological remains should exist as silent witnesses of these cycles. And they do: in fact, we know these cycles well, because we call them the 11,000-year solar cycle. So, what exactly is the 11,000-year solar cycle?

By conducting soil analyses throughout the world and taking ice samples in the arctic regions, periods of around 11,000 years with different climate conditions and temperature can be distinguished. Throughout the world, between these 11,000-year periods, there were very short, intense periods of enormous volcanic eruptions, gigantic global floods and magnetic confusion as magnetism lost its direction. This magnetic confusion was discovered because lava retains the magnetic direction from the time when it solidifies, and lava stones with different magnetic directions have been discovered from those brief periods. So the scientific community knows that the climate and temperature on Earth stayed stable for 11,000 years, after which a great global apocalypse of volcanic eruptions, earthquakes, earth movements, tsunamis and magnetic instability suddenly occurred. After this brief disaster, a new stable climate and temperature would emerge, albeit different from the previous ones. But is the time period of 11,000 years correct? Does climate change occur every 11,000 or every 12,888 years?

We can only solve this problem by examining the research methods used to determine the duration of the solar cycle. On one hand, years can be counted in ice layers by looking at ice crystals, which are formed differently depending on the temperature during crystallisation. The change from summer to winter causes a change in the structure of the ice. However, this only applies to short periods, and not to long periods, during which ice layers may melt, or be squeezed together etc. A large number of factors make this research method rather imprecise for determining the duration of long periods.

The method used to determine the 11,000-year solar cycle was the carbon 14C procedure, discovered by Charles F. Libby in 1949. He noticed that plants, animals and humans not only stored normal carbon 12C in their bodies during their lives, but also radioactive carbon 14C, which comes from nitrogen. When plants, animals and humans die, this 14C starts to decay with a half-life of approximately 5,568 years, whereas the normal carbon remains intact. This phenomenon allows us to determine the age of every unearthed bone, piece of wood or plant seed on the basis of the ratio of normal carbon to radioactive carbon. The age of earth and ice layers can be determined from the age of the biostructure found within it. The structure of the ice in which the dead organism was found, the types of fauna and flora in those layers etc. indicate the former temperature.

Libby's method became the standard measure of time for archaeologists. However, it falls down when used to determine long periods: the inventor assumed that the atmosphere always contained the same percentage of 14C. This appears to be incorrect. The chemist Charles Wesley Ferguson from the University of Arizona concluded that the percentage of radioactive carbon in the atmosphere was clearly different before and after 1500 BC. Because of this, the organisms living at that time had different ratios of 14C. He deduced this from comparative research between the growth rings of 4000-year-old American sequoias and the 14C dating method. His research shows that all remains from that time, and earlier, must have been older than the 14C dating method indicates. A colleague of Ferguson, Hans E. Suess, calculated how "fast" the 14C atomic clock is running. He came to the conclusion that a site dated at 1800 BC using the 14C method actually originated in approximately 2500 BC. This gives a difference of 700 years. Despite the fact that these scientific studies and proofs are recognised in scientific circles as being very accurate, this correction factor has not yet been applied in order to determine the length of the 11,000-year solar cycle. If we take the previous remarks into consideration, then a period dated at just over 11,000 years using 14C becomes, by extrapolation using Suess's correction factor, 12,888 years! The 11,000-year solar cycle and the 12,888-year half-precession appear to be exactly the same cycle! Their periods are the same length.

So the long solar cycle of 11,000 years is actually the half-precession cycle of 12,888 years. Between these stable periods, we can find evidence of floods, tsunamis, volcanic activity and land movements, as well as fossils from buried animals and plants, at locations all over the world. Lava takes the magnetic direction from the atmosphere at the moment when it solidifies. In the brief apocalyptic period, the magnetic direction seems to be totally confused. After the apocalypse, the magnetic direction once again refers to the usual magnetic north, as the geographic poles switch places as a result of the magnetic poles switching places. However, after the Earth turns upside down, the magnetic poles may be slightly different, by as much as 30°. We call this a pole jump. How is this possible?

Earth's magnetic poles aren't identical to its geographic poles, nor do they correspond 100% to the magnetic poles of the fast solar wind; instead, Earth's magnetic poles are between the geographic poles and the poles of the fast solar wind. This is because, on one hand, the magnetic pole tries to move to the associated geographic pole because of the Earth's rotation. On the other hand, the magnetic pole would like to be 23°26' away from the geographic pole in order to align with the fast solar wind. Because of the Earth's rotation, the magnetic pole should move in a 24-hour cycle, but it doesn't, as the permanent Earth magnet is not flexible enough. The Earth's mass partially resists it, though we observe small 24-hour rotations of the magnetic poles, while over a period of one year, the poles decline continuously in the opposite direction of the Earth's rotation, which seems logical. The differences in position between the poles of the fast solar wind and of the permanent Earth magnet are compensated for by the elasticity of the Earth's atmosphere. So we observe small movements from Earth's magnetic poles, which demonstrate that the magnetic poles can and will move if the fast solar wind changes position, but that the Earth's inner elasticity is not sufficient to cause them to move to the same extent as the changed poles of the solar wind. Fortunately, the elasticity of the atmosphere can compensate for the differences; otherwise, our Earth would exhibit a 24-hour wobbling movement.

However, if the magnetic direction of the fast solar winds starts to dominate from the opposite direction, Earth's elastic atmosphere will no longer be able to compensate for the very different locations of the poles of the fast solar wind and the poles of the Earth magnet. In fact, they would repel each other with magnetic force, causing the inner Earth magnet to turn upside down in order to be magnetically aligned once again with the magnetic fast solar wind. The inner Earth magnet is not sufficiently elastic to suddenly move upside down without taking the whole Earth mass with it.

So, in order to connect the new magnetic poles of the fast solar wind with the poles of the permanent Earth magnet, the Earth magnet will turn upside down, sweeping the whole Earth along with it. This rotation will stop wherever Earth's magnetic pole finds optimal connection with the pole of the fast solar wind. This doesn't need to be exactly 180 degrees, as previously the magnetic pole was not in exactly the same position as the pole of the fast solar wind because it was compensated by the elasticity of the Earth's atmosphere. But if the Earth doesn't turn exactly 180°, the inclination of the Earth's axis will no longer be 23°26'. Exceptionally, at certain points in history, the conditions were such that the magnetic direction could change without sweeping the whole of Earth's mass with it, although this happened rarely: about once every 750,000 years. Secondly, the inner elasticity of the Earth will shift the Earth's crust during this sudden rotation. If this inner elasticity of the Earth shifts the Earth's crust suddenly by 8°, for instance, the geographic poles will suddenly shift by 8°. Both factors – the Earth turning upside down, which will not be by exactly 180° and which will therefore change the inclination of the Earth's axis, and the shifting of the Earth's crust – will redesign the climate and temperature everywhere on Earth for the next stable period of 12,888 years. So the Earth experiences stable climate and temperature periods of 12,888 years, after which there is a global apocalypse as the Earth turns upside down. After this huge disaster, everywhere on Earth will again experience a stable period, but with a different climate and temperature from before. A new world has been born.

In his excellent work, the Path of the Poles, the scientist Charles Hapgood used a substantial amount of documentation to prove these geological facts and the cyclical jumps of the geographic and magnetic poles, which is widely recognised in the scientific world, and received words of praise from highly acclaimed scientists such as Albert Einstein. Although it is accepted, science doesn't provide a clear explanation about this matter; unfortunately, this silence hides the truth and neglects its importance. I do understand that the correct explanation is not possible because of current scientific misunderstandings. So anyone who explains it would have to produce an almost fantastical thesis, which would contradict so many current beliefs that it would not be taken seriously. What's more, accepting cyclical global apocalypses as fact is against our human nature, which makes us strive for safety and survival. It would also overthrow our basic beliefs about our existence, such as territorial rights of countries and of property, our stable, planned society and family, our belief in government protection etc. Although it is the truth, it simply cannot be accepted. This disastrous phenomenon makes us blind.

Some scientists came up with a reason for the jumps in the geographic and magnetic poles during the most recent disaster of 10,865–10,500 BC. Analysing their idea, it seems ridiculous, but because it is the only idea, it has gained some acceptance in scientific circles. In short, their position is that it was such a cold era that in the Arctic North, ice layers became so high that because of the Earth's rotation and the unevenly distributed mass of these ice layers, they may have suddenly turned the Earth by about 15°. Any reasonable person would raise an eyebrow. However, their idea that the jump was only 15° and not 165° makes it more acceptable in human minds, causing them to forget that the cause of both events should be enormous. Additionally, the idea that it was a single event and not cyclical can make it easier for us to accept it – emotionally rather than logically. However, they forgot that it is a cyclical event, which means that every 12,888 years, ice layers should become so high and be distributed so unevenly that it causes the Earth to tilt.

This seems too coincidental. We are close to the end of one of these 12,888-year periods, so where are these huge ice layers now? The Himalaya, with a height of 8 km, cannot influence the stability of the Earth. So how high would these ice layers have to be and how unevenly would they have to be distributed at both the North Pole and the South Pole? But crucially, why do they believe that there were warmer and colder periods, as the Sun does not become warmer and colder cyclically?

However, if the Earth's axis of inclination changes and the geographic poles suddenly shift to new geographic poles as a result of a shift in the Earth's crust, then there will be a change in climate and some regions will shift towards the Arctic while others will shift towards the equator. This means that some regions will become colder than before the precession disaster while others will become warmer than before the precession disaster. Scientists assume that there are temperature fluctuations during the long solar cycle of 12,888 years, as they measured these fluctuations by analysing samples. But they made a serious error of deduction. The Sun didn't suddenly become warmer or colder; some regions became warmer or colder because of the shift in the Earth's crust. So the temperature fluctuations they measured were in fact due to the shift in the Earth's crust.

Between 10,865 and 10,500 BC, the Ice Age suddenly faded away in North America and Europe, while at the same time Antarctica was covered in ice, having been partially or totally free from ice before 10,865–10,500 BC. The rich flora and fauna of Siberia was also suddenly frozen during this same period of 10,865–10,500 BC. The Sahara, now known for its desert, was a fairly densely populated area before the precession disaster, with many lakes. Around 10,865–10,500 BC, the Sahara suddenly started drying out. Lake Chad, on the border of Niger, Nigeria and Chad, shrank dramatically.

The lake at Agorass n'Essoui dried up completely, forcing the people of Adrar Bous to seek their fortune elsewhere. Even the water level of Lake Victoria, somewhat further south, fell drastically. The rainy climate of Egypt became a dry desert climate between around 10,865 and 10,500 BC.

To give an example regarding the flora and fauna: how do you explain the fact that a tropical mammal like the mammoth was suddenly frozen while eating tropical vegetation, along with the tropical plants in full bloom found next to him? Did spring suddenly leap into perpetual winter? This is no fairy tale! In Siberia, hundreds of frozen mammoths were found with half-chewed flowers in their jaws. These discoveries have been dated to the end of the last Ice Age, some 12,000 years ago. However, instead of becoming warmer, it seems that Siberia became ice-cold. Baron Toll, a polar explorer, discovered a 21-metre-thick layer of fossilised remains on Bolshoi Lyakhov, one of the Siberian islands. Among them were the remains of the woolly rhinoceros, the mammoth, the American ox, deer, horses, antelopes, sabre tooth tigers, sheep, and flora such as a 30-metre-long Alnus fruticosa with mature fruit, green foliage and seeds. It could well be assumed that the mammoth was a polar animal, even though its skin was as thick as that of today's elephants, with hair that contained no oil glands, which would be perilous in the cold weather. But how do you classify the other discoveries, remains of tropical fauna and flora, such as fruit trees that presumably grow in a mild climate? And how would a mammoth on an ice sheet find its daily requirement of over 100 kg of green food? And how could they suddenly be frozen alive?

The Avesta, the sacred book of Zoroastrianism, which came to us from the ancient Iranian people, tells us of the perilous consequences of the shift in the Earth's crust. The story is based in the area around Airyana Vaejo, homeland of the "Aryan" or Indo-Iranian people: "In those days the

Airyana Vaejo enjoyed a mild and productive climate with seven months of summer and five of winter. Rich in wildlife and in crops, its meadows flowing with streams, this garden of delights was converted into an uninhabitable wasteland of ten months' winter and only two months' summer as a result of the onslaught of Angra Mainyu, the Evil One..."

"The first of the good lands and countries which I, Ahura Mazda, created was the Airyana Vaejo... Then Angra Mainyu, who is full of death, created an opposition to the same, a mighty serpent and snow. Ten months of winter are there now, two months of summer, and these are cold as to the water, cold as to the earth, cold as to the trees... There all around falls deep snow; that is the direst of plagues."

According to the book "Fingerprints Of The Gods" by Graham Hancock:

"When Angra Mainyu sent the 'vehement, destroying frost' [quoting the Bundahishn], he also 'assaulted and deranged the sky' and had mastered 'one third of the sky and overspread it with darkness'."

Ahura Mazda calls a meeting of the gods, and tells us that "'the fair Yima, the good shepherd of high renown in Airyana Vaejo', attended this meeting with all his excellent mortals."

"It is at this point that the strange parallels with the traditions of the biblical flood begin to crop up, for Ahura Mazda takes advantage of the meeting to warn Yima of what is about to happen as a result of the powers of the Evil One. 'And Ahura Mazda spake unto Yima saying: 'Yima the fair... Upon the material world a fatal winter is about to descend, that shall bring a vehement, destroying frost. Upon the corporeal world will the evil of winter come, wherefore snow will fall in great abundance...' 'And all three sorts of beasts shall perish: those that live in the wilderness, and those that live on the tops of the mountains, and those that live in the depths of the valleys under the shelter of stables.

Therefore, make thee a var [underground enclosure] the length of a riding ground to all four corners. Thither bring thou the representatives of every kind of beast, great and small, of the cattle, of the beasts of burden, and of men, of dogs, of birds and of the red burning fires. There shalt thou make water flow. Thou shalt put birds in the trees along the water's edge, in verdure which is everlasting. There put specimens of all plants, the loveliest and most fragrant, and of all fruits the most succulent. All these kinds of things and creatures shall not perish as long as they are in the var. But put there no deformed creature, nor impotent, nor mad, neither wicked, nor deceitful, nor rancorous, nor jealous; nor a man with irregular teeth, nor a leper."

According to the Avesta, Airyana Vaejo was now a place where "the stars, the moon and the sun are only once a year seen to rise and set, and a year seems only as a day..." The ancient Indian epic, the Mahabharata, says: "At Meru the sun and the moon go round from left to right every day, and so do all the stars... The day and night are together equal to a year to the residents of the place..." This reminds us of conditions at the North and South Poles.

In the next chapter, we will analyse more of the world's features before the last precession disaster.

CHAPTER 10
THE WORLD BEFORE THE LAST PRECESSION
DISASTER OF 10,865–10,500 BC

We are now aware of the discovery of and evidence for the half-precession cycles separated by global apocalypses, which were explored in previous chapters, but what do we actually know of the world before the last disaster in 10,865–10,500 BC?

It is difficult to say much about the Earth's axis, as we have very little evidence, but it is likely that the Earth's axis was inclined less than today's 23°26', as we read in different legends that there was less difference between summer and winter. In the north of North America and Western Europe, there was an ice age, so we can assume that the geographic pole was located in the centre of that region. And if the Earth's axis was tilted less, the conditions would be even worse than at the actual poles. The other geographic pole was somewhere between Australia and Antarctica, which meant that Antarctica was totally ice-free, or at least partially ice-free on the South American side. The north of Russia, including Siberia, had a more moderate climate, allowing mammoths and many other mammals to live easily without any instinct to head south.

Because the geographic pole was in the north of Northeast America, this part of the continent was sparsely populated. However, across the rest of the Earth, there must have been impressive civilisations, connected with one another. This may be the only explanation for people from very different parts of the world having a lot of things in common: words and languages, knowledge of the precession and the tendency to regard it as the most important thing, similar myths and legends etc. These common features are a mystery to today's scientists.

According to various legends, the first civilisation arose 75,000 to 78,000 years ago as Mu or Lemuria. Around 50,000 BC, Lemuria was almost completely destroyed. However, this civilisation held on for 52,000 years until it was finally totally destroyed as a result of a pole reversal 26,000 years ago, or around 24,000 BC. The Lemurians constructed many megalithic buildings. Their greatest achievements were said to have been their wisdom, their education and the fact that they spoke one language. 52,000 years is equal to two complete precession movements or four global disasters. The fourth appears to have been fatal. It is said to have caused Mu to sink. As Mu sank into the ocean, the water level of the oceans rose drastically.

The Mediterranean Sea also used to be much lower. At the point where the Nile flows into the Mediterranean Sea, it used to flow further to the north and then to the west. Where the Mediterranean Sea is now, there existed an advanced civilisation: the Osirian civilisation. This civilisation was also submerged during the great disaster in around 10,865–10,500 BC. It is an archaeological fact that there are dozens of known sunken cities on the bottom of the Mediterranean Sea. The Minoan and Mycenaean civilisations on Crete are said to have descended from them. The Osirian civilisation was well known for its construction of huge earthquake-proof megalithic structures. A Hermitic text of Ancient Egyptian origin talks with admiration of "almost god-like people and their devotion to collecting knowledge, who lived before the Great Flood, and whose civilisation has been destroyed."... "Magnificent remains on earth made by their hand will bear witness, though their tracks will disappear as the cycle continually renews the Earth."

There are hundreds of ancient texts about the Atlantic civilisation. We shall look at a few. The following description is taken literally from the Oera Linda book, a collection of Frisian traditions: "During the whole summer, the sun hid itself behind the clouds, as if unwilling to shine upon the earth. In the middle of the quietude, the earth began to quake as if it was dying. The mountains opened up to vomit forth fire and flames. Some of them sank under the earth while in other places mountains rose out of the plains… [Atland] disappeared, and the wild waves rose so high over the hills and dales that everything was buried under the seas. Many people were swallowed up by the earth, and others who had escaped the fire perished in the waters."

Atlantis, also called Poseid, brought technology and the organisation of the community to an extraordinarily high level. Atlantis was destroyed in three stages. The first part sank around 50,000 BC. A second part was underwater from around 24,000 BC. Finally, during the last great disaster, in around 10,865–10,500 BC, Atlantis was swallowed up by the water.

The Samoan islanders assert that "the sea arose suddenly, and, in a stupendous catastrophe of nature, the land sank into the sea". The Tahitian traditions state that in ancient times Tagaroa, the principal god, who according to their mythology is the creator of the world, being angry with men on account of their disobedience to his will, "overturned the world into the water", causing the entire earth to sink into the water except for a few "*aurus*", constituting the present clusters of islands.

The book "Cataclysm! Compelling Evidence of a Cosmic Catastrophe in 9500 B.C." states: "The Mixtecs of Mexico in their myths speak of a now-vanished land to the east of the American coast: 'In a single day all was lost, even the mountains sank into the water… subsequently there came a great deluge in which many of the sons and daughters of the gods perished.'" Even the Selungs of southern Burma refer to such a continent: "…formerly their country was of continental dimensions. But the daughter of an evil spirit threw many rocks into the sea. Thereupon the waters rose and swallowed up all the land. Everything alive perished, except what was able to save itself on one island that remained above the waters. The forefathers of the Selungs then practised great magic and this caused the waters to fall." Then the Selungs turned to other islands "than their sunken continent", and have inhabited these ever since.

The most well-known author to describe the Atlantic culture in great detail was Plato. Despite the fact that the story of Atlantis appears to be pure fiction, Plato was only interested in purely philosophical, scientific and historical works. Fairy tales and stories were not his cup of tea. Why do his historical reports, dozens of pages long, with detailed descriptions of the culture, temples and dynasties etc. seem to be fiction? Is it because they do not fit into our modern scientific framework? By contrast, his other works are considered masterly gems… Plato repeats many times that his reports are truly fact, despite looking like a myth. In fact, you find anecdotes in various works, although the most detailed descriptions are taken from only two of Plato's dialogues, Timaeus and Critias. In these books, it appears that the texts were handed down by Plato's grandfather, Critias, who knew the texts via his great-grandfather Dropides, who heard the story from Solon, a legislator from Athens who, while travelling in Egypt, had questioned the Egyptian priests about the earliest known history. The ancient Egyptian culture, with its massive library in Alexandria, had a wealth of ancient historical reports. The loss of this treasure is a result of many wars and acts of destruction. The priests told Solon what they knew about the Great Flood. One of the old priests, who went by the name of Sonchis of Sais, began speaking to Solon. He was vexed at the new city state (i.e. Ancient Greece) and their ignorance and denial of the past. During the time of the Ancient Greek civilisation, you could compare the united city state of the Greeks to the present-day United States: powerful, well-organised, technically advanced, although its culture and history were hardly ancient.

Sonchis explained the following to Solon: "O Solon, Solon... in mind you are all young; there is no old opinion handed down among you by ancient tradition, nor any science which is hoary with age. And I will tell you why: There have been, and will be again, many destruction of mankind arising out of many causes; the greatest have been brought about by the agencies of fire and water, and other lesser ones by innumerable other causes. There is a story, which even you have preserved, that once upon a time Phaeton, the son of Helios, having yoked the steeds in his father's chariot, because he was not able to drive them in the path of his father, burnt up all that was upon the earth, and was himself destroyed by a thunderbolt. Now this has the form of a myth, but really signifies a declination of the bodies moving in the heavens around the earth, and a great conflagration of things upon the earth, which recurs after long intervals... After Zeus killed Phaeton with his thunderbolt, he released the flood in order to put out the fire, after which he positioned the son of the sun in the sky as a morning star. At such times those who lived upon the mountains and in dry places were more liable to destruction than those who dwelt by rivers or on the seashore... When, on the other hand, the gods purge the earth with a deluge of water, the survivors in your country are herdsmen and shepherds who dwell on the mountains, but those who, like you, live in cities are carried by the rivers into the sea..."

The Egyptian priest explained to Solon that during this catastrophe the literature of man had been lost and for this reason the Greeks were unaware of the real horrors of the past. He told him that in some periods man had existed in large numbers and in other periods in small numbers. All the events of ancient history were recorded in Egypt, and the Greek civilisation originated from only a few seeds that survived the great catastrophe in which almost everyone died. "You and your friends from the friendly cities are descended from the few survivors that remained, but you know nothing about it because so many succeeding generations left no record in writing. Only in myths have you preserved memories of the last great disaster, though there were various great recurring disasters."

In his "Politicus", Plato stresses that we should not ignore this disaster. He writes: "I mean the change in the rising and setting of the sun and the other heavenly bodies, how in those times they used to set in the quarter where they now rise, and used to rise where they now set... the god at the time of the quarrel, you recall, changed all that to the present system as a testimony in favour of Atreus." He continued: "At certain periods the universe has its present circular motion, and at other periods it revolves in the reverse direction... Of all the changes which take place in the heavens this reversal is the greatest and most complete... There is at that time great destruction of animals in general, and only a small part of the human race survives."

In the dialogue "Critias", Critias quotes the words of Solon in a very detailed description of everything related to Atlantis, even down to the names and periods of the emperors, the geographical description, the fauna and flora, the army and the political organisation etc. I shall restrict myself to a few passages that tell of the fall of Atlantis at the time of the world catastrophe.

"... 9000 was the sum of years which had elapsed since the war which was said to have taken place between those who dwelt outside the Pillars of Heracles and all who dwelt within them..." Atlantis was an island "larger than Libya and Asia together" (by Asia they meant the Middle East: Iraq, Saudi Arabia, Syria, Jordan, Israel, Lebanon, Kuwait, Yemen, United Arab Emirates etc.) "... there occurred violent earthquakes and floods; and in a single day and night of misfortune all your warlike men in a body sank into the earth, and the island of Atlantis in like manner disappeared in the depths of the sea. For which reason the sea in those parts is impassable and impenetrable, because there is a shoal of mud in the way; and this was caused by the subsidence of the island." "Many great deluges have taken place during the nine thousand years... and during all this time and through so many changes, there has never been any considerable accumulation of the soil coming down from the mountains, as in other places, but the earth [Atlantis] has fallen away all round and sunk out of sight." "For the fact is that a single night of excessive rain washed away the earth... at the same time there were earthquakes, and then occurred the extraordinary inundation..."

Proclus confirmed that Crantor too had visited Sais in Egypt, 300 years after Solon. The Egyptian priests also showed Crantor the hieroglyphs written on gold pillars, corroborating Plato's work. The details of the history of Atlantis appeared to be correct.

Manetho, an Egyptian chronicler, confirmed the existence of these gold pillars. These pillars were made by Thoth just before the flood so that the knowledge of the civilisation would not be lost in the great cyclical disaster. Josephus, a Jewish historian living in the time of Christ, also mentions that Seth

(= Thoth) had made two pillars in which the knowledge had been engraved so that it would not fade away after the great disaster. Josephus also claimed that those pillars still existed in the land of Siriad. The Roman Herodotus personally saw these two pillars in the temple of Hercules in Phoenicia. Alexander the Great also witnessed them several times.

The Egyptian pyramid texts tell in detail of the people of Atlantis using the name "Shin Wr". Arnobius, a Christian bishop of the fourth century AD, said that the great catastrophe that destroyed human civilisation had totally devastated the island Atlantis of Neptune (i.e. the sea-god), as well as many other nations. The Maya say of their genesis that they originated from a mysterious island called Aztlan. Aztlan... Atlantis... They were driven away by volcanic eruptions that resulted in their motherland sinking into the sea. Their voyage is documented in the Codex Boturini and other writings. Hindu traditions talk of a sunken far-away island called Atala. Atala... Atlantis... Atlantis was one of the seven islands of an island group. The Atlantic Ocean also got its name from the island of Atlantis. Furthermore, Plato, Herodotus, Aristotle, Hecataeus of Miletus, Scylax of Caryanda etc. have all used this name. To finish this chapter, I will mention that Greek myths described the seven islands as the seven daughters of the Titan Atlas. The Atlantides were also called the Pleiades and are commemorated in the constellation of similar name.

In the next chapter, we will analyse ancient maps in order to discover where Atlantis was located before the last apocalypse of 10,865–10,500 BC.

CHAPTER 11
IS THERE ANY EVIDENCE OF ATLANTIS BESIDES THE MYTHS AND LEGENDS?

According to descriptions, Atlantis must have been a group of islands in the Atlantic Ocean, between the Americas and Europe–Africa. The biggest island in this Atlantic group must have had a diameter of 3,000 km. This Atlantic group of islands sank in one night during the precession disaster, which featured volcanic eruptions. Although most of the evidence has been lost because of the submersion and the volcanic eruptions, we can still prove it.

In addition to myths or rare archaeological utensils that have been discovered, there is something very interesting that we would like to focus on: ancient world maps showing geological areas that were supposedly unknown at that time. The best example is the Oronteus Finaeus map of 1532. The most famous is the world map compiled by the admiral Piri Reis of the Ottoman–Turkish navy. There are many more examples, however, such as Philippe Buache's world map from 1737.

What is so special about these old maps? For example: until the 20th century, the geological details of Antarctica were unknown to science because this continent was covered by a layer of ice. These details were only discovered in the high-tech age, as a result of soundings taken by satellites. However, the geological details of Antarctica were already drawn on old maps such as the one made by Oronteus Finaeus, even though Antarctica has been covered continuously with ice since 10,865–10,500 BC. So the civilisation that made these maps must have visited Antarctica before 10,865–10,500 BC, when Antarctica was ice-free.

These maps clearly show geographical areas such as the mountains, rivers, lakes and seas of Antarctica, North and South America and other parts of the world, which should not have been known at that time. The Piri Reis map was drawn in 1513, i.e. before the discovery of America, yet it already shows the coast of America. This map is a redrawn summary of about fifteen older maps he had in his possession. Alexander of the Two Horns, as Alexander the Great was nicknamed, described these maps in the fourth century BC.

However, if you take a more critical look at the map, some geographic details do not seem to correspond to our maps. Of course, there will have been changes due to the precession catastrophe. For instance, the fact that America was nearer to Europe–Africa before the disaster, and that the disaster tore them further apart, a fact that we will see later on. However, there is also another reason for the differences: old maps such as the one compiled by Piri Reis used a much more precise technique to project the world onto a map than our projection technique. The projection technique we use nowadays is based on a projection of a sphere with Greenwich as the central point. But a three-dimensional sphere cannot be projected onto a two-dimensional surface without introducing "tears". By pulling these tears together, we end up with huge deformations, which are worse for regions located far away from Greenwich.

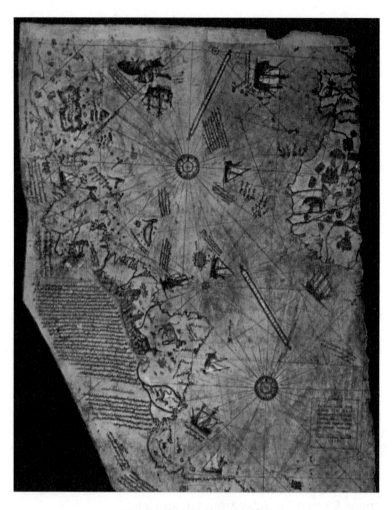

Fig. 28: Piri Reis map (1513)

On old maps like the Piri Reis map, a different projection technique has been applied. These maps used a multipoint projection instead of a two-dimensional spherical projection. What is a multipoint projection? Distances in various directions are projected from one particular point or position. Calculated distances to other locations are projected in all directions – sometimes as many as twenty different directions. Because of this, there is no deformation of the distances from that point or position, and it produces a rather good reflection of reality. Finally, many point projections, i.e. from different points or positions in the world, are glued together to make one multipoint projection, like the different pieces of a soccer ball. In our two-dimensional projection, this results in huge deformations, which accumulate the further you go from Greenwich, while in a multipoint projection the deformations do not accumulate, though there are single deformations in areas that are less important. So in multipoint projections, deformations are avoided when one travels from city to city on the measured routes or map lines, which is not possible with our two-dimensional spherical projection. So the multipoint projection is more realistic and this feature is very important for trading civilisations with long trading routes, especially with ships and (theoretically) aircraft, though it is not important for primitive civilisations.

The positions of the point projections onto the Piri Reis map are incomprehensible. These points or positions are situated in different places in the water of the Atlantic Ocean. This is totally absurd. It means that measurements of thousands of kilometres were taken in many different directions, always starting from the same point in the water, several kilometres deep. It is not only impossible to do so, but also totally pointless. And how can one determine this point or position in the water precisely without the help of the satellites we have today? The only possible, logical reason is that land, or an island, existed at that point. This would make it both feasible and reasonable to draw a point projection from that location. This point projection must have been made by a great civilisation that is no longer known, and which had long navigation routes, and whose islands apparently disappeared suddenly following a huge disaster in the Atlantic Ocean.

Let's take another look at the myths and stories surrounding Atlantis. Atlantis had a moderate climate all year round, thanks to the ground warmth and warm water sources. This is caused by the fact that the Earth's crust was thin, which in turn was due to the fact that the Americas and Europe–Africa were torn apart from each other after the time of Pangaea. The inner convection streams beneath the islands of Atlantis were strong, which caused the Atlantic ridge to be pushed upwards, so that parts of the Atlantic seabed were above sea level, forming the islands of Atlantis. So the thin Earth's crust and the strong inner convection streams meant that Atlantis always had a beautifully warm climate, although it was in a very precarious geological situation. In fact, this may be where the story of Adam and Eve came from. They lived in a paradise where it was always warm, so there was no need for clothes. They lived well, though they could not touch the Tree of Life, which represented the pillar that supported the sky and whose apples represented the stars. However, when the cardinal point symbolised by the winged snake arrived, the precession disaster occurred, and they were banished from Earth's paradise to a place where it was no longer warm, and they needed to wear clothes. The new world was born on that date. There was no good reason to blame the women, or Eve; this was just a religious invention, designed to dominate women because they were believed to represent evil. The ocean around the Atlantic islands was probably not as deep as it is now, and the Americas and Europe–Africa were positioned closer to each other.

The movement of the crust when the Earth turned upside down during the last precession disaster tore open the thin crust at the Atlantic ridge, which was under a great deal of pressure, causing the Americas and Europe–Africa to lose their connection to each other and move apart, just like when two people are each pulling on one end of a rope and the rope breaks. Huge volcanic eruptions took place. The Great Flood was not just a story. As the continents drifted apart, there was much less mass present on the surface of the Atlantic, which suddenly became much larger, and this caused the Atlantic ridge to suddenly sink several kilometres in just one night. We will look at these features in the next chapter.

CHAPTER 12
HOW DID THE EARTH TURN UPSIDE DOWN
IN 10,865–10,500 BC?

In previous chapters, we explained why the Earth turned upside down in around 10,865–10,500 BC and what the world was like before this disaster. The question in this chapter is how the Earth turned upside down at that time.

In around 10,865–10,500 BC, the Earth turned upside down, after which the geographic poles were located in their present position and the inclination of the Earth's axis was 23°26'. It makes logical sense that when the Earth's crust moved over a surface that was not an exact sphere (since the Earth is a little squashed at the poles), volcanic eruptions, earthquakes, landslides, the collapse and creation of mountains, submersion and emergence of islands, tornados, tsunamis, huge floods and huge fires occurred all at once. However, this precession apocalypse was more catastrophic than previous precession disasters. When the Earth turned upside down in around 10,865–10,500 BC, the thin crust of the Atlantic ridge could no longer withstand the pressure of the inner convection streams below it or of the force pushing the Americas and Europe–Africa apart. The Atlantic ridge tore open from the far north to the far south. The middle of the Atlantic crust ripped apart, causing the Americas and Europe–Africa to lose their connection to each other and move apart, just like when two people are each pulling on one end of a rope and the rope breaks. The Americas and Europe-Africa-Asia suddenly drifted a large distance away from each other, with the Americas moving much more since they are much lighter than the other three continents, which are anchored together. That's why, at that moment, there were volcanic eruptions throughout the Atlantic islands and that's why the Atlantic islands sank to an ocean floor several kilometres deep in one night, as the mass of the Atlantic crust and layer was distributed across a greater surface. This is the origin of the Great Flood, which we will explore in the next chapter. Today, the great scar caused by the Atlantic region being ripped open is still visible on satellite photos and Google Earth. The enormous scar created by the stretching that took place between the Americas and Europe–Africa is clearly recognisable. This is why the continents are now further away from one another than is shown on the Piri Reis maps.

*Fig. 29: scar and stretching of the floor
of the Atlantic Ocean ©Google Earth*

This event has even been proven by geological findings, including, for instance, the report of the French Geologist P. Termier. Having been commissioned to work on the construction of the transatlantic telecommunication lines, the professor took samples from the bottom of the ocean, 900 km north of the Azores. These were basalt rocks of the tachylite type, a glassy lava taken from the seabed, around three kilometres deep. What is so special about this lava? Seemingly nothing, were it not for the fact that this type of coagulated lava can only be formed in open air, and not in water. In other words, thousands of samples of lava, taken from the deep floor of the Atlantic Ocean, appear to have solidified in open air, because in water they would have solidified differently. And it becomes even more interesting if we look at the time period in which these lava samples were created. The special feature of this type of rock is that it loses its glassy shine 15,000 years after being created. However, the lava rocks were still in good condition, which means that they originated from a period less than 15,000 years ago, from islands or a small continent in the centre of the Atlantic Ocean, which must have sunk three kilometres below sea level as a result of great volcanic eruptions. An event like this, less than 15,000 years ago, can only refer to the precession disaster in around 10,865–10,500 BC. It is frightening to note that geological research corresponds to the features created by the last precession disaster.

The Americas moved in a westerly direction as if they were let loose from a rope that connected them with Europe–Africa. This sliding caused a turning movement in South America, because the western side of the continent became partially stuck, causing the former east coast to be tilted upwards, several kilometres high. On the Andes plateau, it is possible to observe a 600-kilometre-long coastline of beach and shellfish, which is now situated at a height of between 3,700 and 3,900 metres, and which dates back to around 10,865–10,500 BC. Another piece of tangible, concrete evidence can be found on the border of Peru and Bolivia. There we find Lake Titicaca at a height of 3,800 metres above sea level. It is approximately 222 metres long and 112 metres wide and, in certain places, is up to 300 metres deep. Despite the fact that Lake Titicaca is situated at a height of over three kilometres, the area around the lake is littered with seashells. This leads us to suspect that the whole plateau once rose up from the seabed. Until now, Lake Titicaca has maintained a "sea ichthyofauna". Although the lake is now hundreds of kilometres from the ocean, the fish and shellfish are much more saltwater than freshwater varieties. Weird and wonderful creatures have been found in the nets of fishermen, such as specimens of the Hippocampus (seahorse), different varieties of Allorchestes and other kinds of sea life. The lake has an undeniable sea origin and was dammed when the Andes rose.

Furthermore, this rise cannot have taken place very long ago. First, ruins have been discovered on the bed of Lake Titicaca. Secondly, there are a number of mysterious old cities on the plateau of the Andes. Tiahuanaco is situated within this region, approximately 20 km south of the lake at a height of over 3 km. The ruins of Tiahuanaco show evidence of a port, complete with extensive docks.

No one knows why these cities were suddenly deserted. The Polish researcher Arthur Posnansky, who did more than 50 years of research on this site, dated Tiahuanaco to between 15,000 and 10,500 BC! Their architectural skill is also rather a mystery. Adjacent stones were joined together internally by a kind of bronze alloy in the form of a double barb. It is remarkable that the same technique can also be seen in the architecture of other ancient civilisations all over the world, for example in Egypt and Crete! The stones were not simple bar-shaped stones like the ones used to-day, but appeared to be cut into different shapes and fitted together so as to increase resistance to earthquakes. You cannot even slide a blade between the joints... a finesse that exceeds modern skills.

One can now imagine clearly how such a great continental shift can cause a great flood like the one described in the Bible. In the next chapter, we will deal with the Great Flood.

CHAPTER 13
THE LAST PRECESSION DISASTER CAUSED
THE GREAT FLOOD

In the previous chapter, we discovered the sudden continental shift caused by the Earth turning upside down, which also led to the sinking of the great islands of Atlantis. It is therefore evident that this created a kilometre-high tsunami that ran across the whole world. There are still a large number of geological remnants of this tsunami. Geological research in the Scablands in North America, carried out by J. Harlen Bretz, proves that during the period of 10,865–10,500 BC, an enormous tsunami rolled from one coast to the other. This conclusion was derived from landscape features and specific geological details, such as the water cyclones within the tsunami, which had drilled enormous wells in hard rocks. On the basis of these measurements, they came to the conclusion that the tsunami would have been at least 250 metres in height, but probably as much as one kilometre in height. This is enormously high. Modern geologists could not comprehend what may have caused a kilometre-high tsunami in around 10,865–10,500 BC. Because of this, they came up with a fantastical explanation that somewhere there was an enormous dam, which burst and caused this kilometre-high tsunami. But because no dam of this sort has been found, they imagined a kilometre-high layer of ice in the so-called Ice Age. The huge quantity of ice melted, though the edges remained solid and formed a natural dam. When the natural dam burst, the water flowed away in a kilometre-high tsunami from one coast to another, covering a distance of around 4,000 to 5,000 kilometres. It is hard to imagine that anyone would believe this fiction to be reality, but it has until now been accepted by science, purely because of the geological evidence of the tsunami and the lack of any other explanation. What a mass of water must it have been! It seems more of an ocean shift than a melting layer of ice. Even though there were no other explanations, it is unnecessary to insult our intelligence with the idea of a burst ice dam. The tearing open of the Atlantic plateau together with the sinking of the Atlantic islands and the sudden movement of the continents provide a much more logical explanation for the kilometre-high tsunami from 10,865–10,500 BC.

But surely all the peoples of the world have legends that explain this? "People heard and saw an enormously high wall of water approaching the land from a great distance, and nothing and nobody was spared. Only a few who had escaped to caves in the highest mountains were safe." The Egyptian sun-god Ra declared of himself: "I am he who created the water and the great flood." Referring to some literal translations of the Epic of Gilgamesh: "for one day the south-storm blew... gathering speed as it blew, submerging the mountains... No one can see his fellow... nor can the people be recognized from heaven... The gods were frightened by the deluge ... and, shrinking back, they ascended to the heaven of Anu... six days and seven nights... blows the flood wind, as the south-storm sweeps the land... When the seventh day arrived, the flood south-storm subsided in the battle..."

Or Genesis 7:17–24: "The flood continued forty days on the earth. The waters increased and bore up the ark, and it rose high above the earth. The waters prevailed and increased greatly on the earth, and the ark floated on the face of the waters. And the waters prevailed so mightily on the earth that all the high mountains under the whole heaven were covered. The waters prevailed above the mountains, covering them fifteen cubits deep. And all flesh died that moved on the earth, birds, livestock, beasts, all swarming creatures that swarm on the earth, and all mankind. Everything on the dry land that in whose nostrils was the breath of life died. He blotted out every living thing that was on the face of the ground, man and animals and creeping things and birds of the heavens. They were blotted out from the earth. Only Noah was left, and those who were with him in the ark. And the waters prevailed on the earth 150 days."

Old Tamil texts tell of a cataclysm, with a mythical great flood that destroyed cities such as Tenmaturai, Kapatapuram and Maturai, which was rebuilt after this flood. When Norwegian engineers wanted to build a dyke structure in Maduru Oya, they discovered in the same place an ancient dyke structure, which had been totally erased from history, just like what happened at Egypt's Nasser Lake.

All peoples knew of the flood, although I shall only give a handful of examples here, taken from the book "Und die Sintflut gab es doch" by Edith and Alexander Tollmann. The Eskimo described the flood as follows: "Long ago, the ocean started to rise all at once, until all the land was covered. The water streamed over the mountain tops, and the ice floated over it." I could not have put it better myself. From this, you can even deduce which way the Earth was turning. The stories of the Pawnee and Wichita Indians indicate that the oceanic flood fell over the low land of the western part of the Canadian Shield in a southerly direction: "The water came from the northwest over the earth." This is precisely the same direction in which, according to scientific observations, the magnetic poles shifted. Moreover, before this terrible event they saw "birds and land animals travelling from north to south." This detail cannot be ignored. Migratory birds, migratory sea animals and some land animals have senses based on magnetism. They could perceive a gradual reversal of the magnetic field some days in advance. There is no other possible explanation for this fact.

Terrifying news of the rolling oceanic tidal wave was handed down in two versions by the Navajo Indians of California: "Finally it happened one morning, when they arose, that something appeared in the east, and in the south, north, and west; it was like a mountain wall with no openings, stretching around them. They were surrounded by water; you could not go through it or over it by boat, and everyone fled. They ran around in a circle around until they reached the heavens."

"One day people noticed that the animals were all running from the east to the west. This lasted for several days. On the fourth day, when daylight appeared, they saw something bright, white and sparkling in the east, and they sent grasshoppers out as spies, to see what was going on. They came back before evening, saying that a tremendous flood was approaching. The people gathered and bemoaned their fate. The next morning the flood arrived, like a mountain filling the whole horizon, except in the west..." Perhaps even more shocking is the story of the Choctaw Indians from the Oklahoma–Mississippi area in the south-eastern part of North America: "For a long time, the whole earth was completely dark. The medicine men of the Choctaw watched for daylight for a long time, until they finally despaired of ever seeing it again. And all the people were very unhappy. Finally, they noticed a light in the north, and they celebrated with a great feast, until they discovered that waves were approaching, as high as mountains, which killed all the people..." This frightening view of the tidal wave was also described by the Pima Indians: "In an instant, a terrible thunder and an awful cracking sound could be heard, and a green hill of water rose up above the plain. For a second it seemed to stand up, and then it was split by a fierce flash of lightning and rolled forwards like a big animal. When the morning came, no-one could be seen alive, except for one human – if it was a human." The Peruvians also described the thundering noise that accompanied the oceanic tidal wave when it crashed down over the inland areas. It is rather eerie that the legends have given such an accurate account of reality.

Here is an example from the Chinese annals during the time of Emperor Yahou: "The sun did not go down for ten days. The world was enveloped in flames, and in their vast extent the waters crashed over the highest mountains, threatening the heavens with their floods. The water of the ocean was heaped up and cast upon the continent of Asia; a great tidal wave swept over the mountains and broke in the middle of the Chinese Empire. The water was caught in the valleys between the mountains, and the land was flooded for decades." When a natural catastrophe on this scale happens, the sea is pulled out of its bed, mountains rise up and rivers change their course, and the traces of civilisation disappear… "Emperor Yahou sent his disciples to the different parts of China, and even to Indo-China, in order to find out where the north, west, east and south were now located, by observing how the sun now rose and set and how the stars moved… At this time, the miracle was said to be that the sun did not rise for ten days, the woods were on fire…" A Taoist text says: "The breath of heaven is out of harmony. The four seasons do not observe their proper times."

Old traditions from Peru are almost identical: "For a period of five days and five nights, the sun was not in the sky, and the ocean burst its banks and flowed with enormous force over the continent; the whole surface of the Earth was changed in one almighty disaster." Manuscript Troano and other documents of the Maya describe a cosmic catastrophe during which "the ocean fell on the land, and a terrible hurricane swept the earth. The hurricane broke up and swept aside every city and forest. Volcanoes were erupting, tidal waves raged over mountaintops and constant winds threatened the existence of the human race. And so many kinds of animals were made extinct. The appearance of the Earth changed. Mountains collapsed; other mountains were raised up, and protruded above the raging water that came from the oceans. Countless rivers lost their beds. A wild tornado moved through the debris descending from the sky. In the darkness, swept up by the wind, dust fell from the air, which, along with the fire and the water, contributed to the destruction of the world. For five days the sun did not shine."

Or to say it using the argumentation of Cicero: "De quo autem amnis natura consentit, id verum esse necesse est." The generality of the traditions of the great flood proves that this catastrophe must have really taken place.

In the same way, in late spring, a tsunami of ice-cold water flowed to the north of Russia and Siberia, which almost immediately froze its flora and fauna until the present day, which is why, for instance, a large number of frozen mammoths were discovered while they were still rather fresh. However, it was not only tsunamis of water but also a heavy sludge of water mixed with sand, soil, ash, lava and similar substances, that rolled across certain areas of land. The flora and fauna were powerless to resist and were swept away, seized together and buried in that sludge. Even nowadays, archaeologists are surprised by the fact that many animals, both prey and hunters, can be found a few metres from one another, as if buried alive: hundreds at the same time at thousands of sites across the world. As a child, I tried to imagine how this could happen, based on the world I knew. The only picture I could conjure up was that of a rock falling on a surprised animal and burying it forever as a fossil. How else do you explain an animal being buried without being eaten? There are not even any traces of hungry insects. But the animals at the thousands of sites all over the world were surprised and buried, especially in the period of around 10,865–10,500 BC, sometimes hundreds at the same time, some still with their prey half in their mouth, others in the middle of giving birth, most with no broken bones.

Only a big wave of sludge consisting of sand and cement could bury these groups of animals intact and uneaten in a mass grave. This sand–cement sludge is perfectly comparable with modern "cement flows" from erupted snow-covered volcanoes. This brings a misunderstanding to light: all over the world these layers, sometimes several metres thick, are estimated to be very old, while the time it took for the entire layer to be formed is estimated at between 10,000 and 100,000 years, even though we know now that this happened in a matter of one or two days. How else can you explain the fact that there are trees with their roots under the 10,000-year layer, their trunk in the 10,000-year layer, and their top above the 10,000-year layer?

The book "Darwin's Mistake" by the German chemical engineer Hans J. Zillmer gives lengthy lists of these findings, backed up by tangible evidence, logical explanations and photographs. You cannot ignore the thousands of such archaeologically "inexplicable" discoveries and simply set them aside. Nevertheless, that is how modern science deals with it… the easiest solution is to ignore what cannot be explained.

Besides this, we know now about the existence of half-precession periods separated by global apocalypses during which the Earth turns upside down. An interesting question is: "What is our present situation in this cycle?" This is something we will look at in the next chapter.

CHAPTER 14
WHAT IS OUR PRESENT SITUATION
IN THE HALF-PRECESSION CYCLE?

As the half-precession cycle, which causes the Earth to turn upside down every 12,888 years, is very important to us, the question arises: When can we next expect the Earth to turn upside down? On the basis of dates from archaeological and geological findings, precession calendars and traditions, I estimate that the next cardinal point will be between 2023 and 2388 AD. However, I'm not a clairvoyant: if I'm wrong by just 5 years, then we will already be in trouble right now. The only way to be sure is to make astronomical observations.

I refer to the official report "Planetophysical state of the earth and life" sponsored by the Millennium Group and written by Dr. Alexey N. Dmitriev: "The current developments in our solar system are caused by the non-uniformity of matter and energy in the part of the universe through which our solar system is travelling. On its journey through galactic space, our heliosphere travels in the direction of the solar apex in the Hercules constellation. On its way it has met non-homogeneities of matter and energy in the form of ions. In this kind of interstellar plasma dispersed across space there are magnetised strip structures. The transition of the heliosphere through this structure has led to an increase of the shock wave in front of our solar system from 3 to 4 Astronomical Units to 40 Astronomical Units or more. This thickening of the shock wave has caused the formation of a cohesive plasma in a split belt, which has led to a remodelling of the plasma in our solar system, and finally to a breakthrough into the planetary belts. This breakthrough consists of a kind of matter and energy exchange originating in interplanetary space and passed on to our solar system. In response to this exchange of matter/energy, we have observed a number of large-scale events."

Dr. Dmitriev says: "We must emphasise the significant increase in scientifically recognised magnetic anomalies in relation to the Earth's magnetic reorganisation. Their significance is due to the fact that these world anomalies stem from a magnetic source that is completely independent of the Earth's core magnetism."

A little further on in his report, he continues: "We also have to take into account the actual increase in the polar cusp angle (i.e. the polar openings at the magnetic north and south poles), which reached 45° in 1990. While this angle normally fluctuates around 6°, in recent years it has varied between 26° and 45°. Both this widening and the increased solar activity mean that more matter and radiation from the Sun are rushing into these openings, causing the Earth to warm." So, at the poles, the magnetic field is shaped like a funnel. The angle of the opening is normally 6°. In recent decades, this angle has increased heavily and is now fluctuating between 26° and 45°. This is normal when the poles start to counter an opposing magnetic direction.

Dr. Alexey N. Dmitriev of the Russian National Scientific Academy in Siberia continues: "The climatological and biological processes on Earth are a direct consequence of, and are linked to, the general processes of complete change that are taking place in our solar system. We need to start focusing our attention on this, and we have to understand that the climate changes on Earth are only a part, or a link, of a whole chain of events taking place in our heliosphere. Moreover, the situation in the heliosphere is completely attributable to factors of external, interstellar, cosmic origin, and is therefore assumed to be caused by a fundamental, self-preserving kind of pendulum movement. This pendulum movement is astrophysical in nature and is responsible for the continuous evolution within our universe."

According to Dr. Dmitriev, at the moment, the same phenomena are undoubtedly taking place as when the dinosaurs died. This point in time is characterised by a huge change in the climate of the Earth and weather patterns, and perhaps by a reversal of the geographic poles. The Earth is rapidly evolving towards a period of unstable temperatures, comparable with that of around 10,865–10,500 BC. This similarity was uncovered through the analysis of ice samples drilled from the ice layers in Greenland. These ice samples have shown that, at that time, the temperature had increased by 7 degrees, the rainfall had increased by a factor of between 3 and 4, and the quantity of dust particles had increased a hundredfold. According to the Russian Academic Dr. Kondratyev, we are now evolving towards climatological chaos. Dr. Dmitriev's research evidences that: "The critical point during previous periods of reversal of the poles has been a consistent worldwide increase in the level of the oceans (10–150 metres), caused by contractions, accumulations and stretching of the crust layers worldwide. The water level of the oceans is therefore connected with the forces in action during the expansion and contraction movements of the crust layers." And further on... "In addition, the melting of the ice caps at the poles will cause the water level to rise, with the result that coastlines will be redrawn."

The plasma in the heliosphere is increasing, as observed by NASA and the Russian intelligence services. Dr. Dmitriev of the Russian National Academy of Science subsequently announced that the luminous energy at the leading edge of our heliosphere is now 100 Astronomical Units deep, in a position where the depth of the luminous energy is normally 10 Astronomical Units. This increase in plasma, or energetic movements, affects the atmosphere of the planets in our solar system. A study carried out by Dr. Mike Lockwood of the Rutherford Appleton Laboratory showed a 230% increase in the magnetic field of the Sun during the last 100 years. Solar activity has also increased, which inevitably worries the heliophysicists. In the Earth's atmosphere, the formation of a supplementary HO gas has been observed, for inexplicable reasons. A thin atmosphere is also developing on Mars, where it was previously non-existent. This new atmosphere was the reason why a mirror panel on the Mars Observer broke off in 1997. After all, the space probe was not protected against a possible atmosphere. In addition, an unusual concentration of ozone is developing on Mars. During the Moon landing in 1969, NASA claimed that there was no atmosphere present. Now it looks as if there is a thin atmosphere developing with a depth of 6,000 km, primarily consisting of what Dmitriev refers to as "Natrium". On Venus, there has been a strong increase in gases containing sulphate. On Pluto, it has been observed that the atmospheric pressure has more than doubled in the short time it has been studied, i.e. from 1988 onwards. An increase in the atmosphere has also been detected on Jupiter, Uranus and Saturn. On Saturn, atmospheric rings have also been observed recently. The planets also look brighter; this is very noticeable with Venus, for instance. On Jupiter, the energetic charge has risen so high that a visible tube of ionised radiation can be detected between Jupiter and its moon Io.

The north–south direction of the fast solar wind is weakening significantly. I refer to the work of the professional geologist and researcher Gregg Braden. His idea is that we are getting nearer and nearer to the end of a cycle. We are seeing rapid changes in the fundamental parameters of our

Earth, which we once thought constant. He expresses the magnetic field strength in Gauss on a scale of 0 to 10, where 10 is the strongest. It is possible to deduce from fossils and minerals that the magnetic field once had a strength of 10 Gauss. 2,000 years ago, the magnetic field had weakened to 4 Gauss. By 1998, its strength had dwindled to 0.4 Gauss and it is still decreasing.

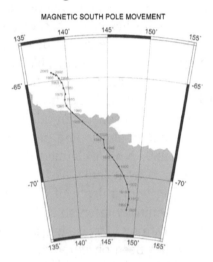

Fig. 30: magnetic south pole movement

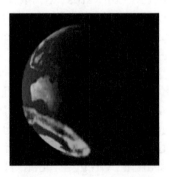

*Fig. 31: increased aurora australis lights
(photo from the official NASA internet site)*

At the South Pole, the southern fast solar wind is increasing so much that Earth's magnetic south pole is being pushed away further to the north. Because of this increased southern fast solar wind, a lightning crown can be observed in the south, and this has been called the aurora australis. That's why the hole in the ozone layer first appeared in the Southern Hemisphere even though most pollution is in the Northern Hemisphere. And although this pollution, the CFCs and methane gas that were supposedly the reason for the hole in the ozone layer, decreased substantially, the hole keeps on growing year after year. As a result of the collisions caused by the fast solar winds, the frequency of the vibrations of the Earth's magnetic field is increasing. For a long time, people were convinced that the frequency remained constant at 7.8 Hz. This heartbeat was attributed such importance for the proper functioning of our bodies that it was taken into account in space flights made by astronauts. Gregg Braden has demonstrated that this heartbeat has suddenly risen to 11.2 Hz and, in some locations on our planet, reaches peaks of up to 14 Hz.

The layers of gas and plasma are undergoing the heaviest changes: plasma is forming in the ionosphere, while in the magnetosphere we are observing an increase in the number of magnetic storms and, in the atmosphere, an increase in the number of cyclones. These atmospheric phenomena used to be rather rare, but now they are occurring more frequently, even changing in nature. These magnetic changes also cause tension in the Earth's crust. Volcanic and seismological activity is increasing in accordance with what has been observed in the last 400 years. From 1963 to 1993, the number of natural disasters increased by 410%. Between 1875 and 1975, volcanic activity rose by 500% and, since 1973, earthquakes have increased by 400%. In addition, the increasing temperature on Earth can no longer be attributed to human activity; it is actually linked more closely to the collision of the north and south fast solar winds, with all the consequences that entails. If polluted gas layers trapped the Sun's radiation so that it could not escape from the Earth, how could it reach the Earth? It's a vicious circle! Greenpeace reported that in 2001, at the location of the magnetic north pole, the ice cap had melted for the first time in human memory.

On the basis of astronomical and scientific data in relation to the Earth's magnetism, virtually all universities claim that a reversal of the magnetic poles is very near. We cannot escape it even if we prefer to ignore it and continue living our usual lives. When the Macedonian king, Alexander the Great, came across the Celts during his conquests northwards in 335 BC, he asked them what they feared the most, in order to intimidate them psychologically. The answer was very different from what he expected. The tough Celts feared only that "the sky would fall on their heads and that the stars would lose their direction". The details of what was said later that night in the Greek leader's tent have been lost. It must have left a big impression as the people who were there were still talking about it thirty years later. Modern scientists spent a long time turning this mysterious answer over in their minds and finally realised that this seemingly simple philosophy defined an outlook on life – an outlook that was shared by other peoples with a similar psychic structure: like the Archaic Greeks (the heroes of Homer) or the Turkish people from around Lake Baikal. This raises the suspicion that the Celts had said something that was extraordinarily important to them. It was so important that it had a big effect on the leader of the half-civilised Macedonian band. Based on this, Alexander established the final northern border and returned to conquer the east and the south in search of wealth and knowledge among the oldest civilisations, such as the Egyptians.

In next chapter, I will express my personal views on these facts.

CHAPTER 15
WHAT CAN WE DO ABOUT
THE PRECESSION DISASTER?

In the previous chapters, we discovered the existence of the 12,888-year periods separated by apocalypses in which the Earth turns upside down. Furthermore, we discovered the horrific extent of this disaster and the fact that we are very close to the next catastrophe. So what can we do in the face of this terrible upcoming event? It's a pity that the correct date of this event is not certain. It is estimated at between 2023 and 2388 AD, which makes us less interested in making preparations for such an event. We often prefer to leave things up to fate and foolishly assume that it will not happen in our lifetime. Volcanoes and super volcanoes will start to erupt in all their glory. Movements of the Earth's crust will cause earthquakes whose magnitude will require additional values to be added to the Richter scale. Mountains will collapse and other mountains will emerge, while the Earth's crust tears open and fold in on one another. Lands and islands will be at the mercy of the sea, swallowed up by high tsunamis, and the remaining lands will be burned to the ground if they are not covered by a great flood. Hurricanes will blow away what remains on the Earth. The features of the precession disasters are terrible, brutal and enormous, and we can only guess what it will be like this time.

If the current magnetic north pole becomes the geographic North Pole, then we will have a new Ice Age in the Laptev Sea in the nord of Sacha-Jacuzia (Russia), and its inhabitants will be forced to flee as refugees to the south. The south

Pole will be shifted a little into the direction of the South Atlantic Ocean. After a precession disaster of this kind, it will be difficult to find or produce enough food for the survivors. But what will make this precession catastrophe more horrific than previous disasters is the release of radioactivity from destroyed nuclear power plants and nuclear facilities. We can hardly dare to hope that mankind will survive it, though even if it does, the knowledge and progress of our civilisation may not survive and, just as before, this precession catastrophe will be known through myths and legends.

As a highly developed civilisation, we should immediately and unconditionally start to prepare ourselves for such a threat, but I doubt that this will ever happen, because our reaction is typical of the kind of intelligence that humans have. If mankind was purely rational, we would only use causal connections to make decisions. Everything would be studied rationally in relation to everything else, allowing the truth to emerge and ensuring that the right decisions and efforts are made.

However, mankind is not an intelligent civilisation consisting of only pure rational minds. Rationality clearly exists but is often buried by two other forms of intelligence. On one hand, mankind has emotional intelligence. Egoism, emotions, feelings and intuition often take priority over purely rational ideas, which means that rational decisions are not always taken. On the other hand, the intelligence of mankind is rather an indoctrinated intelligence, in which most people have become wise by learning from one another rather than by means of their own rational questioning of everything around them. Much of our knowledge has been learned without being questioned. And what society as a whole believes has so much credibility and power over a single rational person that it is regarded almost as a sin if one dares to be critical of a common belief.

Of course, indoctrination has many advantages, because

this type of education allows people to become "wise" quickly, learning ideas without putting a great deal of energy into questioning all the aspects in order to arrive at these ideas. Furthermore, a society is more connected if everyone's beliefs and ideas are similar, which means that people with similar beliefs and ideas will be accepted much more easily than critical spirits, even if these critics are right. However, indoctrination also has a big disadvantage. The beliefs and ideas of a society can also move in the wrong direction and eventually no longer correspond to reality. These incorrect beliefs and ideas cannot be rectified easily as they may be the basis on which many other beliefs and ideas are built. And if a large society has been indoctrinated in these incorrect beliefs and ideas in the form of religion and science, then it is almost impossible to reject them. New beliefs and ideas will be made ridiculous, will be censored or will be neglected because of the fear of looking foolish or being punished.

What's more, religious and political leaders would be unlikely to gamble their position with a risky announcement about the precession disaster. And people prefer not to think about such a destructive event, because it would cause our human minds to suffer. Nevertheless, it is my hope that mankind can stand together and face this natural disaster, because our efforts may save hundreds of millions of people – perhaps even a billion – and may guarantee the continued existence of our civilisation.

FIGURES

Fig. 1: Djeds with each 4 cross bars
Fig. 2: movement and position of our solar system in our Milky Way
Fig. 3: Christian cross not referring to Jesus
Fig. 4: the Ankh
Fig. 5-8: Sumerian cross
Fig. 9: Celtic cross
Fig. 10: the Dragon constellation in the Beijing Ancient Observatory
Fig. 11: Cherub
Fig. 12: Roman Sphinx
Fig. 13: Orthodox cherub
Fig. 14: 4 constellations of the cardinal points and 4 archangels on the ceiling of a Christian church
Fig. 15, 16, 17: the precession cycle, depicted in the allegory as two gods with a fire gimlet
Fig. 18: the Aztec Sunstone
Fig. 19: Hathor as depicted in tombs
Fig. 20: the zodiac in the temple of Hathor at Denderah
Fig. 21-22: the zodiac from the temple of Hathor at Denderah
Fig. 23: the link between the fast solar wind and the magnetic directions of the planets
Fig. 24: the magnetic field of Uranus
Fig. 25: the solar wind in our Solar System
Fig. 26: the interaction between the solar wind and the interstellar plasma

Fig. 27: each half precession cycle, the angle of collisions between the interstellar plasma and the solar plasma switches between north and south
Fig. 28: Piri Reis map (1513)
Fig. 29: scar and stretching on the floor of the Atlantic Ocean ©Google Earth
Fig. 30: magnetic south pole movement
Fig. 31: increased aurora australis lights (photo from the official Nasa internet site)

A FEW OF THE BEST REFERENCES

D. S. Allan & J.B. Delair, Cataclysm, Bear & Company,1997.

R. Bauval & A. Gilbert, The Orion Mystery, London: QPD, 1994.

M. Biglino, La Bibbia non parla di Dio, Mondadori, 2016.

L. Bürgin, La storia proibita, Piemme, 2016.

L. Cozzi, Archeologia Proibita.

G. Hancock, Fingerprints of the gods, Random House, 2001.

Dr.. Hans J. Zillmer, Darwins Irrtum, Langen - Mueller Verlag, 2019.

C. Hapgood, Path of the Pole, Adventures Unlimited Press,1999.

R. M. Schoch, La civiltà perduta e le catastrofi dal sole, XPublishing Srl, 2012.

D. E. Scott, Het elektrisch heelal.

Z. Sitchin, The Stairway to Heaven, HarperCollins Publishers Inc, United States, 2011.

E. and A. Tollman, Und die Sintflud gab es doch: vom Mythos zur historischen Wahrheit, Droemer Knaur, 1993.

J. Van den Driessche, TOE – Theory of Everything.

I. Velikovsky, Mankind in Amnesia, Sidgwick & Jackson Ltd, 1982.

W. Zitman,Van Egypte naar Atlantis, Walburg Pers, 2013.

Google Earth
www.wikipedia.org

Index

Finito di stampare
nel mese di dicembre 2020
presso Rotomail Italia S.p.A. – Vignate (MI)